Assessment Tests for Higher Grade
Chemistry

D. A. Buchanan
(Moray House Institute,
Heriot-Watt University)

J. R. Melrose
(Williamwood High School,
Clarkston, Glasgow)

Published by
Chemcord
16 Inch Keith
East Kilbride
Glasgow

ISBN 1 870570 49 9

© Buchanan & Melrose , 1994

Contents

Note to teachers

The tests are specifically designed to pin-point learning difficulties and to check pupil's understanding of the work covered in the revised Higher Grade Chemistry course. They have been trialled over a number of years and found to be an invaluable aid.

While the tests can be administered to the whole class, it is suggested that they can be more effectively used by pupils working at their own pace in class, during self-study time in school or as homework. The information from the test results can be used to help pupils to plan revision. The answer grid at the back of the book has space for such pupil comments. The test results can also be used by teachers who are interested in assessing individual or class difficulties.

Each test is, by and large, independent of the others and consequently the tests can be used to fit almost any teaching order.

The variation in the length of the tests is a reflection of the different kinds of question which are associated with a particular area of content. Consequently, different allocations of time are required.

Acknowledgement

A number of the questions in the tests come from or have evolved from questions used in the SCE examinations. The publisher wishes to thank the Scottish Examination Board for permission to use examination questions in these ways.

Test 1.1   Rate of reactions (i)

In questions 1 to 20 decide whether each of the statements is

A. TRUE   **B.** FALSE.

1. Increasing the temperature increases the rate of reaction.

2. Lumps of calcium carbonate react faster with acid than calcium carbonate powder.

3. A dilute acid usually reacts faster than a concentrated acid.

4. A catalyst can speed up the rate of a reaction.

5. Milk is more likely to turn sour at 0 °C than at 10 °C.

6. Small potatoes take longer to cook than large potatoes.

7. Plants grow faster in warm weather than in cold weather.

8. Compared with coal dust, lumps of coal burn very rapidly.

9. A catalyst can be recovered chemically unchanged at the end of a reaction.

10. Catalysts can be used in car exhaust systems to speed up the reactions which remove harmful gases.

11. Acetylene burns less rapidly in pure oxygen than in air.

12. Chips cook faster in oil at 300 °C than in oil at 200 °C.

13. A catalyst is used up during a chemical reaction.

14. Reactions involving gases go faster when the pressure is increased.

15. The rate of a reaction is likely to be fastest nearer the end of the reaction.

16. The unit for average rate of change of concentration of a reactant could be mol l^{-1} s^{-1}.

17. For a fixed change in concentration of a reactant, the shorter the time taken, the faster the rate of reaction.

18. All exothermic reactions occur spontaneously at room temperature.

19. All exothermic reactions occur at easily observable rates.

20. For some reactions, the reaction rate can double for every temperature rise of ten centigrade degrees.

In questions 21 to 24 decide whether the catalyst is an example of

A. a homogeneous catalyst   **B.** a heterogeneous catalyst.

21. platinum in the complete combustion of hydrocarbons and carbon monoxide in car exhaust systems

22. aqueous cobalt ions in the reaction between an aqueous solution of Rochelle salt and hydrogen peroxide solution

23. iron in the Haber Process

24. nickel in the hydrogenation of unsaturated oils to saturated fats

Test 1.2   Rate of reactions (ii)

Questions 1 and 2 refer to the graph which shows data obtained from the reaction of zinc with hydrochloric acid.

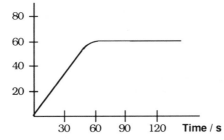

1. What was the total volume of hydrogen produced in the reaction?

    A. $20 \, cm^3$ **B.** $40 \, cm^3$ **C.** $60 \, cm^3$ **D.** $80 \, cm^3$

2. How long did it take for the reaction to go to completion?

    A. 30 s   **B.** 60 s   **C.** 90 s   **D.** 120 s

Questions 3 to 5 refer to the graph which shows how the concentration of a reactant in a reaction varied with time.

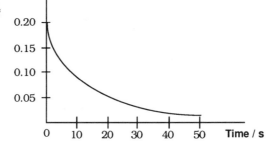

3. What was the initial concentration, in $mol \, l^{-1}$, of the reactant?

    A. 0.05   **B.** 0.10   **C.** 0.15   **D.** 0.20

4. What was the average rate at which the reactant was used up, in $mol \, l^{-1} \, s^{-1}$, in the first 20 s?

    A. 0.0025   **B.** 0.0050   **C.** 0.0075   **D.** 0.0150

5. What was the average rate at which the reactant was used up, in $mol \, l^{-1} \, s^{-1}$, in the period 20 s to 40 s?

    A. 0.00050   **B.** 0.00125   **C.** 0.00250   **D.** 0.01250

6. 1 mol of hydrogen gas reacts with 1 mol of iodine vapour. After t seconds, 0.8 mol of hydrogen remains.

   What is the number of moles of hydrogen iodide formed at t seconds?

   A. 0.2   **B.** 0.4   **C.** 0.8   **D.** 1.6

7. The results of an experiment carried out at 19 $^{\circ}$C involving the reaction between equal volumes of 0.5 mol l^{-1} nitric acid and sodium thiosulphate solution of different concentrations are shown.

Concentration of sodium thiosulphate solution/mol l^{-1}	0.5	0.25	0.125	0.064
Time for the appearance of sulphur/s	13	25	51	104

   On the evidence of these results alone, which statement is correct?

   A. The more concentrated the thiosulphate solution, the longer the time before the sulphur appears.
   B. The more concentrated the nitric acid, the faster the reaction proceeds.
   C. The more concentrated the thiosulphate solution, the faster the reaction proceeds.
   D. The higher the temperature, the faster the reaction proceeds.

8. The continuous use of large extractor fans greatly reduces the possibility of an explosion in a flour mill.

   This is mainly because

   A. a build-up in the concentration of oxygen is prevented
   B. local temperature rises are prevented by the movement of air
   C. particles of flour suspended in the air are removed
   D. the slow accumulation of carbon monoxide is prevented.

9. Two identical samples of zinc are placed in open vessels. Excess of 2 mol l^{-1} sulphuric acid is added to one, and excess of 1 mol l^{-1} sulphuric acid is added to the other. All other conditions are the same.

   Which of the following is the same for the two samples?

   A. the mass lost from the vessels
   B. the total time for the reaction
   C. the initial reaction rate
   D. the average rate of evolution of gas

10. The graph shows the data obtained from three reactions of zinc with a very slight excess of 2 mol l⁻¹ hydrochloric acid.

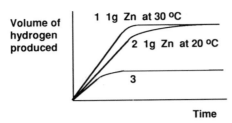

Which statement is true?

A. Increasing the temperature increases the total mass of hydrogen produced.

B. Increasing the temperature has no effect on the initial rate of reaction.

C. Curve **3** would be obtained with 1 g of zinc at 10 °C.

D. Curve **3** would be obtained with 0.5 g of zinc at 20 °C.

Questions 11 and 12 refer to the graph which shows the reactions of three metals with excess of 2 mol l⁻¹ hydrochloric acid.

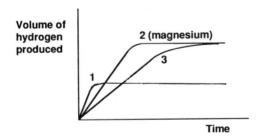

11. Which metal is likely to produce curve 1?

A. lithium   **B.** aluminium   **C.** zinc   **D.** copper

12. Which metal is likely to produce curve 3?

A. lithium   **B.** aluminium   **C.** zinc   **D.** copper

13. During the addition of magnesium to an excess of dilute hydrochloric acid, each of the following was measured and plotted against time on a graph.

   A. the temperature of the solution
   B. the volume of hydrogen produced
   C. the pH of the solution
   D. the conductivity of the solution

   If the reaction was completed in 5 minutes, which of the above was measured to give the graph?

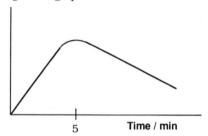

   5   Time / min

Questions 14 to 19 refer to the graphs which show data obtained from reactions of hydrochloric acid.

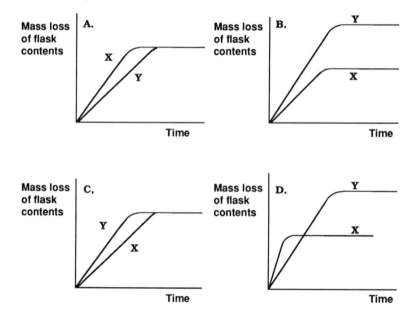

Which graph shows the data likely to be obtained from each of the pairs of reactions?

Contents of flask **X**	Contents of flask **Y**

14. 10 g chalk lumps (excess)
    50 cm^3 of 1 mol l^{-1} HCl(aq)
    20 ^{o}C

    10 g chalk powder (excess)
    50 cm^3 of 1 mol l^{-1} HCl(aq)
    20 ^{o}C

15. 4 cm magnesium ribbon
    50 cm^3 of 2 mol l^{-1} HCl(aq) (excess)
    20 ^{o}C

    4 cm magnesium ribbon
    50 cm^3 of 1 mol l^{-1} HCl(aq) (excess)
    20 ^{o}C

16. 10 g chalk (excess)
    50 cm^3 of 0.1 mol l^{-1} HCl(aq)
    20 ^{o}C

    10 g chalk (excess)
    50 cm^3 of 0.2 mol l^{-1} HCl(aq)
    20 ^{o}C

17. 4 cm magnesium ribbon
    50 cm^3 of 2 mol l^{-1} HCl(aq) (excess)
    20 ^{o}C

    8 cm magnesium ribbon
    50 cm^3 of 1 mol l^{-1} HCl(aq) (excess)
    20 ^{o}C

18. 2 g zinc (excess)
    50 cm^3 of 1 mol l^{-1} HCl(aq)
    20 ^{o}C with catalyst

    2 g zinc (excess)
    50 cm^3 of 1 mol l^{-1} HCl(aq)
    20 ^{o}C without catalyst

19. 2 g zinc (excess)
    50 cm^3 of 1 mol l^{-1} HCl(aq)
    20 ^{o}C

    2 g zinc (excess)
    50 cm^3 of 1 mol l^{-1} HCl(aq)
    40 ^{o}C

20. When copper carbonate reacts with excess acid, carbon dioxide is produced. The curves shown were obtained under two different conditions.

The change from **P** to **Q** can be brought about by

A. increasing the concentration of the acid

B. decreasing the mass of copper carbonate

C. decreasing the particle size of the copper carbonate

D. adding a catalyst.

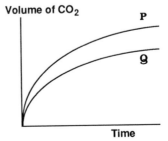

21. The course of the reaction between magnesite (magnesium carbonate) and dilute hydrochloric acid was followed by determining the mass of the reaction vessel and contents as carbon dioxide was evolved. The curves shown were obtained under two different conditions.

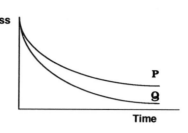

The change from **P** to **Q** can be brought about by

    A. decreasing the concentration of the acid

    B. increasing the temperature of the reactants

    C. increasing the particle size and mass of the magnesite

    D. decreasing the volume of the acid.

22. The graph opposite shows the volume of hydrogen given off against time when an excess of magnesium ribbon is added to 100 cm³ of hydrochloric acid, concentration 1 mol l⁻¹, at 30 °C.

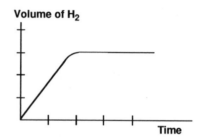

Which graph would show the volume of hydrogen given off when an excess of magnesium ribbon is added to 50 cm³ of hydrochloric acid of the same concentration at 20 °C?

A.
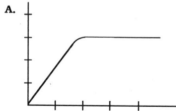

B.
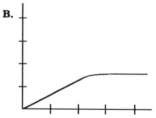

C.
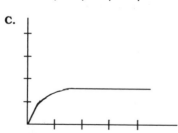

D.
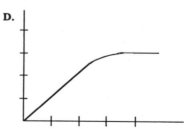

23. Excess zinc was added to 100 cm^3 of hydrochloric acid, concentration 1 mol l^{-1}. Curve **1** refers to this reaction.

Volume of hydrogen produced

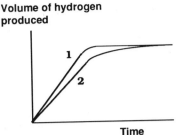

Curve **2** could be for

A. excess zinc reacting with 100 cm^3 of hydrochloric acid, concentration 2 mol l^{-1}

B. excess zinc reacting with 100 cm^3 of sulphuric acid, concentration 1 mol l^{-1}

C. excess zinc reacting with 100 cm^3 of ethanoic acid, concentration 1 mol l^{-1}

D. excess magnesium reacting with 100 cm^3 hydrochloric acid, concentration 1 mol l^{-1}.

24. The graph opposite shows the distribution of kinetic energies of the molecules in a sample of gas.

Number of molecules

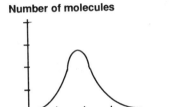

Kinetic energy

Which graph would show the kinetic energies of the molecules when the sample is cooled by 10 K?

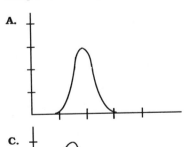

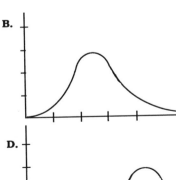

Questions 25 to 26 refer to the graphs.

A.

Rate of reaction

Temperature

B.
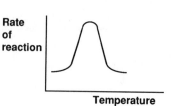
Rate of reaction

Temperature

C.
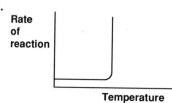
Rate of reaction

Temperature

D.
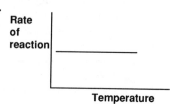
Rate of reaction

Temperature

Which graph could apply to each of the reactions?

25. $C_4H_{10(g)} + 6^1/_2O_{2(g)} \rightarrow 4CO_{2(g)} + 5H_2O_{(g)}$

26. $S_2O_3^{2-}{}_{(aq)} + 2H^+{}_{(aq)} \rightarrow H_2O_{(l)} + SO_{2(g)} + S_{(s)}$

Questions 1 to 3 refer to the energy diagram.

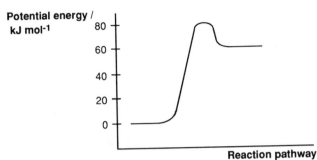

1. What is the enthalpy change, in kJ mol^{-1}, for the forward reaction?

   A. -60   **B.** -20
   C. +60   **D.** +80

2. What is the activation energy, in kJ mol^{-1}, for the forward reaction?

   A. 20   **B.** 60
   C. 40   **D.** 80

3. What is the activation energy, in kJ mol^{-1}, for the reverse reaction?

   A. 20   **B.** 60
   C. 40   **D.** 80

4.

Potential energy

Y

Z

X

Reaction pathway

The energy of activation for the forward reaction is given by

   A. Y   **B.** Z - X
   C. Y - X   **D.** Y - Z.

Questions 5 to 7 refer to the energy diagrams.

A.

Potential energy /
kJ mol⁻¹

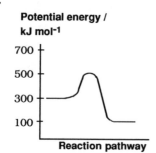

Reaction pathway

B.

Potential energy /
kJ mol⁻¹

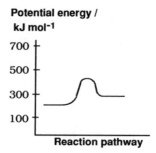

Reaction pathway

C.

Potential energy /
kJ mol⁻¹

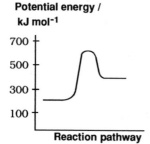

Reaction pathway

D.

Potential energy /
kJ mol⁻¹

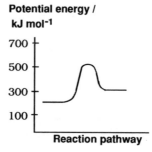

Reaction pathway

5. Which diagram represents the catalysed version of the reaction in diagram **D**?

6. Which diagram represents the forward reaction with the highest energy of activation?

7. Which diagram represents the forward reaction with an enthalpy change of -200 kJ mol^{-1}?

8. The energy diagram for the reaction

   $CO_{(g)} + NO_{2(g)} \rightarrow CO_{2(g)} + NO_{(g)}$

   is shown.

   What is the enthalpy change, in kJ mol^{-1}, for the reaction?

   A. +361
   B. -93
   C. -227
   D. -361

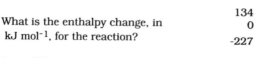

Potential energy /
kJ mol⁻¹

134
0
-227

Reaction
pathway

9.

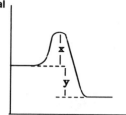

Reaction pathway

The activation energy for the reverse reaction can be represented by

A. **x**   B. **y**

C. **x + y**   D. **x - y**.

10. Which reaction should be most easily reversed?

A. Potential energy

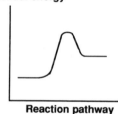

Reaction pathway

B. Potential energy

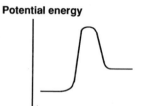

Reaction pathway

C. Potential energy

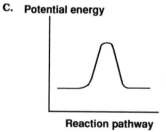

Reaction pathway

D. Potential energy

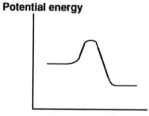

Reaction pathway

11. **Potential energy**   **Potential energy**

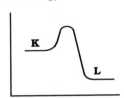   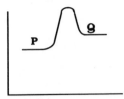

Reaction pathway   Reaction pathway

Which reaction has the greatest activation energy?

A. K → L   **B.** L → K

C. P → Q   **D.** Q → P

Questions 12 to 14 refer to the energy diagram. The unbroken line
represents the reaction $2SO_2 + O_2 \rightarrow 2SO_3$
and the broken line the same reaction under different conditions.

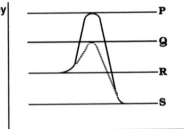

Reaction pathway

12. What conditions are indicated by the broken line?

A. higher pressure   **B.** lower temperature
C. lower concentrations   **D.** use of a catalyst

13. Which of the following represents the interval QP?

A. energy of activation for reaction without a catalyst
B. enthalpy of reaction for reaction without a catalyst
C. bond dissociation energy
D. none of these

14. Which interval represents the enthalpy of the reaction?

A. RP   **B.** PS
C. RS   **D.** QS

15. Which of the following correctly
    represents the activation
    energy (Ea) and the enthalpy
    change (ΔH) for the forward
    reaction?

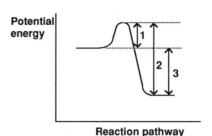

Potential energy

Reaction pathway

	Ea	ΔH
A.	2	3
B.	1	2
C.	1	3
D.	2	1

16. For the reaction $H_2(g) + I_2(g) \rightleftharpoons 2HI(g)$
    the activation energy for the forward reaction is 181.5 kJ mol^{-1} and for the
    reverse reaction is 192.8 kJ mol^{-1}.
    What is the enthalpy of formation, in kJ mol^{-1}, of $2HI(g)$?

    A. +11.3   B. -11.3   C. +374.3   D. -374.3

17. Which of the following describes the effect of a catalyst?

	Activation energy	Enthalpy of reaction
A.	decreased	decreased
B.	decreased	increased
C.	unchanged	decreased
D.	decreased	unchanged

18. For the reaction $N_2(g) + 3H_2(g) \rightleftharpoons 2NH_3(g)$

    which statement about the catalyst is true?

    A. It decreases the rate of the reverse reaction.
    B. It decreases the heat released in the reaction.
    C. It increases the activation energy.
    D. It increases the rate of the reverse reaction.

19. Manganese dioxide speeds up the decomposition of hydrogen peroxide
    because it

    A. increases the enthalpy change
    B. increases the energy of activation
    C. decreases the enthalpy change
    D. decreases the energy of activation.

20. The reaction between oxalate ions and permanganate ions in the presence of hydrogen ions may be summarised:

When a little permanganate solution is added to hot (70 °C) acidic oxalate solution there is a time lag before the purple colour disappears; thereafter, with further additions of permanganate, the colour disappears instantly.

Which statement is a reasonable explanation of the instant disappearance of colour once the initial reaction has occured?

A. The reaction is endothermic.

B. The Mn^{2+}(aq) which is formed catalyses the reaction.

C. The acid is a catalyst for the reaction.

D. The activation energy for the reaction is high.

21 The same reaction was carried out a four different temperatures. The table shows the times taken for the reaction to occur.

Temperature / °C	20	30	40	50
Time /s	60	30	14	5

The results show that

A. a small rise in temperature results in a large increase in reaction rate

B. the activation energy increases with increasing temperature

C. the rate of the reaction is directly proportional to the temperature

D. the reaction is endothermic.

22. A filter paper was dipped into a solution of phosphorus in carbon disulphide. After the carbon disulphide had evaporated, the filter paper caught fire. A filter paper dipped in pure carbon disulphide does not catch fire.

This indicates that

A. the burning of phosphorus has a negative activation energy

B. the evaporation of the carbon disulphide provides the activation energy for the burning of the phosphorus

C. the activation energy for the burning of the phosphorus is attainable at room temperature

D. phosphorus provides the activation energy for the evaporation of carbon disulphide.

23. Liquid petrol does not ignite spontaneously when exposed to the air because

A. the enthalpy of combustion of petrol is positive
B. the reaction between petrol and oxygen requires a catalyst
C. the reactants are in different physical states
D. not enough molecules possess sufficient energy to react.

24. $X_2 + Y_2 \rightarrow 2XY$ (ΔH is negative)

Which deduction can be correctly made from the equation?

A. This is a reaction between gases.
B. The reaction goes to completion.
C. XY is more stable than $X_2 + Y_2$.
D. The reaction will not require heating.

25. Which of the following is **not** a factor which affects the rate of a reaction?

A. concentration of reactants
B. kinetic energies of reactants
C. activation energy of reaction
D. enthalpy change for the reaction

Test 2.1   Structure of hydrocarbons

In questions 1 to 12 decide whether each of the hydrocarbons is

A. an alkane   **B.** an alkene
C. saturated   **D.** unsaturated.

(Note that for each question, **two** responses should be given.)

1. ethane

2. cyclopropane

3. propene

4. 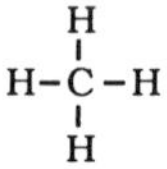
$$H-\underset{\underset{H}{|}}{\overset{\overset{H}{|}}{C}}-H$$

5.

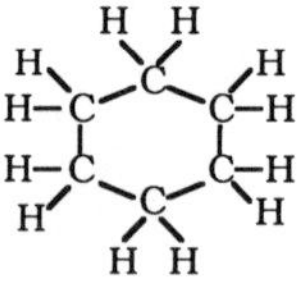

6. 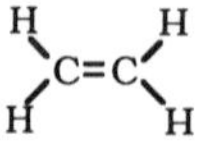
$$\overset{H}{\underset{H}{\diagdown}}C=C\overset{H}{\underset{H}{\diagup}}$$

7. hexene

8. cycloheptene

9. octane

10. 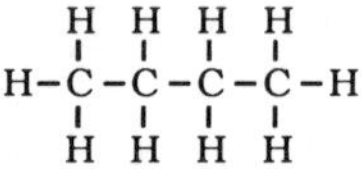
$$H-\underset{\underset{H}{|}}{\overset{\overset{H}{|}}{C}}-\underset{\underset{H}{|}}{\overset{\overset{H}{|}}{C}}-\underset{\underset{H}{|}}{\overset{\overset{H}{|}}{C}}-\underset{\underset{H}{|}}{\overset{\overset{H}{|}}{C}}-H$$

11. 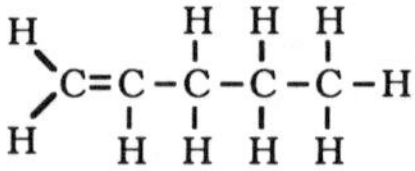
$$\overset{H}{\underset{H}{\diagdown}}C=C-\underset{\underset{H}{|}}{\overset{\overset{H}{|}}{C}}-\underset{\underset{H}{|}}{\overset{\overset{H}{|}}{C}}-\underset{\underset{H}{|}}{\overset{\overset{H}{|}}{C}}-H$$

12.

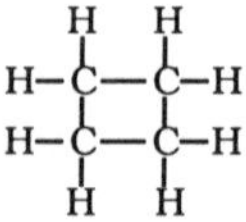

Questions 13 to 18 refer to the naming of hydrocarbons.

A.

        H
        |
   H − C − H
        |
        H

B.

   H   H
    \   /
     C = C
    /   \
   H   H

C.

        H   H
        | |
   H − C − C − H
        | |
        H   H

D.

   H   H
    \ |
     C = C − C − H
    / | |
   H   H   H

E.

        H   H   H   H
        | | | |
   H − C − C − C − C − H
        | | | |
        H   H   H   H

F.

        H   H   H
        | | |
   H − C − C − C − H
        | | |
        H   H   H

G.

        H   H   H   H
        | | | |
   H − C − C = C − C − H
        | |
        H   H

H.

          H   H
           \ /
            C
           / \
   H − C   C − H
      /   \
     H   H

I.

        H   H
        | |
   H − C ─── C − H
        | |
   H − C ─── C − H
        | |
        H   H

J.

   H   H
    \ |
     C ─── C − H
     | |
     C ─── C − H
    / |
   H   H

13. Which is ethane?

14. Which is butene?

15. Which is methane?

16. Which is propene?

17. Which is cyclopropane?

18. Which is cyclobutene?

Questions 19 to 24 refer to the formulae of hydrocarbons.

A. C_5H_{10} **B.** C_5H_{12}

C. C_6H_{12} **D.** C_6H_{14}

What is the formula for each of the hydrocarbons?

19. hexane

20. cyclohexane

21. hexene

22. pentene

23. pentane

24. cyclopentane

25. How many hydrogen atoms are in a straight-chain alkane with 25 carbon atoms?

    A. 48   **B.** 50   **C.** 52   **D.** 54

26. How many hydrogen atoms are in a straight-chain alkene with 12 carbon atoms?

   A. 20   **B.** 22   **C.** 24   **D.** 26

27. How many hydrogen atoms are in a cycloalkane with 16 carbon atoms?

   A. 28   **B.** 30   **C.** 32   **D.** 34

28. How many hydrogen atoms are in a cycloalkene with 21 carbon atoms?

   A. 40   **B.** 42   **C.** 44   **D.** 46

29. Which of the following could **not** be either a straight-chain alkane or a cycloalkane?

   A. C_4H_{10} **B.** C_5H_{10} **C.** C_6H_{12} **D.** C_6H_{10}

In questions 30 to 34 decide which hydrocarbon is **not** a member of the same homologous series as the others.

30. **A.** ethene   **B.** hexene   **C.** butene   **D.** cyclopropane

31. **A.** butane   **B.** methane   **C.** octane   **D.** cyclohexane

32. **A.** C_3H_8 **B.** C_5H_{12} **C.** C_6H_{12} **D.** C_7H_{16}

33. **A.** CH_4 **B.** C_3H_6 **C.** C_6H_{12} **D.** C_8H_{16}

34. Hydrocarbons with a formula mass of :

   A. 16   **B.** 44   **C.** 84   **D.** 100

Questions 35 and 36 refer to homologous series.

   A. CH_2-CH_2 **B.** CH_2=CH_2 **C.** CH_4
   $\quad\,$ | $\quad\,$ |
   $\quad\,CH_2$-CH_2

Which of the hydrocarbons is a member of the same homologous series as each of the following?

35. $CH_3CH_2CH_3$

36. $CH_3CHCHCH_3$

Test 2.2   Reactions with bromine and hydrogen

In questions 1 to 12 decide whether each of the hydrocarbons

A.   does react quickly with bromine

B.   does **NOT** react quickly with bromine.

1. octene

2. hexane

3. butane

4. pentene

5. cyclopropane

6. cycloheptene

7.

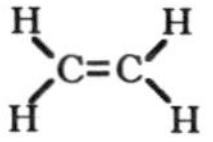

8.

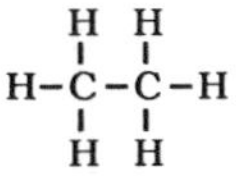

9.

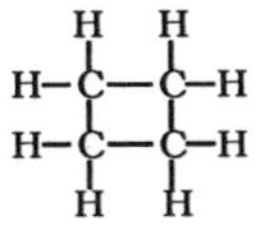

10.

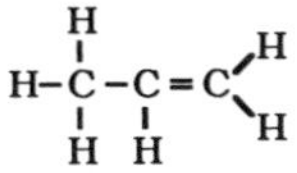

11.

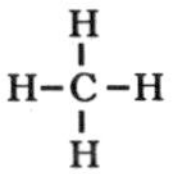

12.

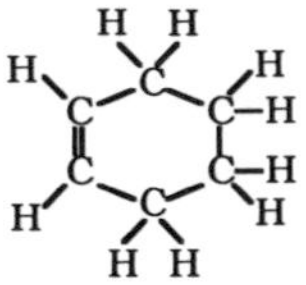

(Note that for questions 13 and 14 more than one response may be correct.)

13. Which of the following represent(s) the product of the reaction between ethene and bromine?

A.

$$\begin{array}{ccc} H & & H \\ & C=C & \\ Br & & Br \end{array}$$

B.

$$\begin{array}{cc} H & Br \\ H-C-C-Br \\ H & H \end{array}$$

C.

$$\begin{array}{cc} Br & Br \\ Br-C-C-Br \\ Br & H \end{array}$$

D.

$$\begin{array}{cc} H & H \\ H-C-C-H \\ Br & H \end{array}$$

E.

$$\begin{array}{cc} Br & H \\ H-C-C-H \\ Br & H \end{array}$$

F.

$$\begin{array}{cc} H & Br \\ H-C-C-H \\ Br & H \end{array}$$

G.

$$\begin{array}{cc} Br & Br \\ Br-C-C-Br \\ Br & Br \end{array}$$

H.

$$\begin{array}{cc} H & H \\ Br-C-C-Br \\ H & H \end{array}$$

14. Which of the following represent(s) the reaction between propene,

$$\begin{array}{ccc} H & H & H \\ & C=C-C-H & \\ H & & H \end{array}$$, and bromine?

A.

$$\begin{array}{ccc} H & H & H \\ H-C-C-C-H \\ Br & H & Br \end{array}$$

B.

$$\begin{array}{ccc} Br & H & H \\ Br-C-C-C-H \\ H & H & H \end{array}$$

C.

$$\begin{array}{ccc} Br & H & H \\ & C=C-C-H & \\ Br & & H \end{array}$$

D.

$$\begin{array}{ccc} Br & H & H \\ H-C-C-C-H \\ H & Br & H \end{array}$$

E.

$$\begin{array}{ccc} H & Br & H \\ & C=C-C-H & \\ Br & & H \end{array}$$

F.

$$\begin{array}{ccc} H & H & H \\ H-C-C-C-H \\ Br & Br & H \end{array}$$

G.

$$\begin{array}{ccc} H & H & H \\ Br-C-C-C-Br \\ H & H & H \end{array}$$

H.

$$\begin{array}{ccc} H & Br & H \\ H-C-C-C-Br \\ H & H & H \end{array}$$

15. A hydrocarbon, molecular formula C_5H_{10}, does **not** quickly decolourise bromine.

Which hydrocarbon could it be?

A. pentane   B. cyclopentane

C. pentene   D. cyclopentene

16. When a molecule of the compound $CH_2 = CH - CH = CH_2$ completely reacts with bromine, the number of atoms of bromine used would be

A. 1   B. 2   C. 3   D. 4.

17. What kind of reaction takes place when butene decolourises bromine?

A. cracking   B. addition

C. oxidation   D. condensation

Questions 18 and 19 refer to the products of the reaction of alkenes with hydrogen.

A. ethane   B. propane   C. butane   D. hexane

18. What is formed when butene reacts with hydrogen?

19. What is formed when $\overset{\displaystyle H}{\underset{\displaystyle H}{>}}C=C\overset{\displaystyle H}{\underset{\displaystyle H}{<}}$ reacts with hydrogen?

20. Which hydrocarbon reacts with hydrogen to form hexane?

A. propene   B. pentane   C. hexene   D. octane

21. What kind of reaction takes place when pentene reacts with hydrogen?

A. hydrolysis   B. reforming

C. hydration   D. hydrogenation

Test 2.3   Systematic naming of hydrocarbons

Questions 1 to 16 refer to the systematic naming of hydrocarbons.
Suggested names are shown.

Decide whether the suggested name for each of the hydrocarbons is

    A. CORRECT   **B.** INCORRECT.

1.
$$CH_3-\underset{\underset{H}{|}}{\overset{\overset{CH_3}{|}}{C}}\!\!-\!\!\underset{\underset{H}{|}}{\overset{\overset{CH_3}{|}}{C}}-CH_3$$

2,3-dimethylbutane

2.
$$CH_3-\underset{\underset{CH_3}{\underset{|}{CH_2}}}{\overset{\overset{H}{|}}{C}}-CH_2-CH_3$$

2-ethylbutane

3.
$$CH_3-CH_2-CH_2-\underset{\underset{H}{|}}{\overset{\overset{CH_3}{|}}{C}}-CH_3$$

4-methylpentane

4.
$$H-\underset{\underset{CH_3}{|}}{\overset{\overset{CH_3}{|}}{C}}-CH_2-CH_2-CH_3$$

1,1-dimethylbutane

5.
$$CH_3-\overset{\overset{\overset{H\diagdown_{}\diagup H}{C}}{\|}}{C}-CH_2-CH_3$$

2-methylbut-1-ene

6.
$$CH_3-\overset{\overset{H}{|}}{C}=\underset{\underset{CH_3}{|}}{C}\!\!-\!\!\underset{\underset{H}{|}}{\overset{\overset{CH_3}{|}}{C}}-CH_3$$

2,3-dimethylpent-2-ene

7.
$$\begin{array}{c}CH_2\!\!-\!\!CH_2\\ |\qquad\;\,|\\ CH_2\!\!-\!\!\underset{\underset{CH_3}{|}}{C}-CH_3\end{array}$$

1,1-dimethylcyclobutane

8.
$$H-\underset{\underset{CH_2-CH_3}{|}}{\overset{\overset{H}{|}}{C}}-\overset{\overset{H}{|}}{C}=C\diagup^{H}\diagdown_{H}$$

3-ethylprop-1-ene

9.
$$CH_3-\overset{\overset{\displaystyle H}{|}}{C}=\overset{\overset{\displaystyle H}{|}}{C}-\overset{\overset{\displaystyle H}{|}}{C}-CH_2-CH_3$$
$$H-\overset{|}{C}-CH_3$$
$$\overset{|}{C}H_3$$

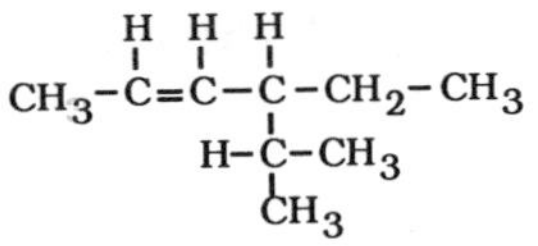

4-ethyl, 5-methylhex-2-ene

10.

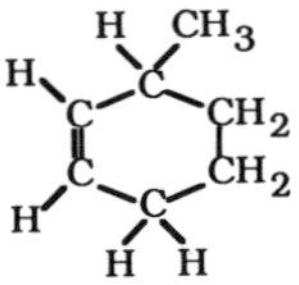

2-methylhexene

11. $CH_3CH(CH_3)CH(CH_3)CH_3$ 2,3-dimethylbutane

12. $(CH_3)_3CH$ methylpropane

13. $CH_3CHC(CH_3)_2$ pent-2-ene

14. CH_2CHCH_3 propene

15. $CH_3CH_2C(CH_3)_2CH_2CH_3$ 3-ethylpentane

16. $(CH_3)_2CCH_2$ but-1-ene

17. Which hydrocarbon has a molecular formula different from that of the other three?

   A. 2,2-dimethyl, 3,3-dimethylbutane
   B. 3-ethylpentane
   C. 2,3-dimethylpentane
   D. 2,2-dimethyl, 3-methylbutane

18. Which hydrocarbon has the same formula mass as 3,3-dimethylbut-1-ene?

   A. $CH_3C(CH_3)_2CH_2CH_3$
   B. $CH_2C(CH_3)CH_2CH_3$
   C. $CH_2C(CH_3)CH_2CH_2CH_3$
   D. $CH_3CH(CH_3)CH(CH_3)_2$

Test 2.4   Isomers (i)

(Note that for some of the questions in the test, more than one response may be correct.)

Question 1 to 3 refer to isomers of alkanes.

A. $CH_3-CH_2-CH_2-CH_3$

B. $CH_3-CH_2-CH_2-CH_2-CH_3$

C. $CH_3-\underset{\underset{CH_3}{|}}{CH}-CH_2-CH_3$

D. $CH_3-CH_2-CH_2-CH_2-CH_2-CH_3$

E. $CH_3-\underset{\underset{}{}}{\overset{\overset{CH_3}{|}}{CH}}-CH_3$

F. $CH_3-\underset{\underset{CH_3}{|}}{\overset{\overset{CH_3}{|}}{C}}-CH_3$

G. $CH_3-CH_2-CH_2-\underset{}{\overset{\overset{CH_3}{|}}{CH}}-CH_3$

Pick out **all** the compounds that are isomers of each of the structures.

1.   **A**

2.   **B**

3.   **D**

Questions 4 to 6 refer to isomers of alkanes with the formula C_5H_{12}.

A.
```
    H H H H H
    | | | | |
H - C-C-C-C-C - H
    | | | | |
    H H H H H
```

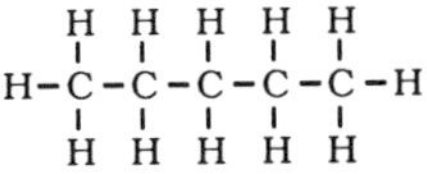

B.
```
    H H H
    | | |
H - C-C-C - H
    |   |
    H   H
    H - C - H
    H - C - H
        |
        H
```

C.
```
    H H
    | |
H - C-C - H
    |   |
    H   H
    H - C-C - H
        |
        H
    H - C - H
        |
        H
```

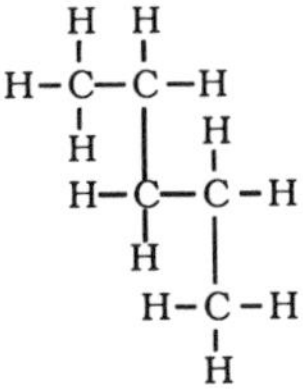

D.
```
        H
        |
    H - C - H
    H   |   H
    |   |   |
H - C - C - C - H
    |   |   |
    H   H   H
    H - C - H
        |
        H
```

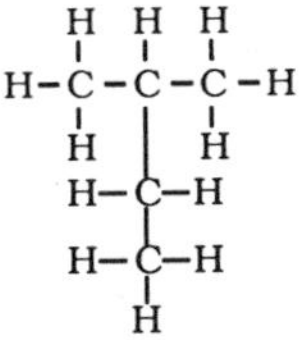

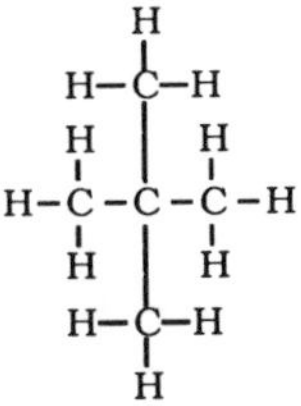

E.
```
        H
        |
    H - C - H
    H   |   H H
    |   |   | |
H - C - C - C-C - H
    |   |   | |
    H   H   H H
```

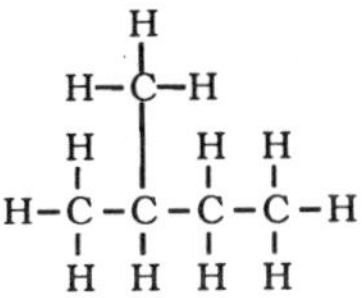

F.
```
    H H H H
    | | | |
H - C-C-C-C - H
    | |   |
    H H   H
        H - C - H
            |
            H
```

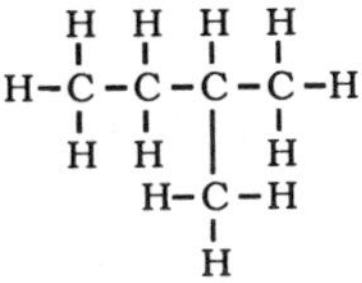

Pick out **all** the compounds that are **not** isomers of each of the structures.

4. **A**

5. **B**

6. Pick out **all** the compounds that are isomers of the following structure.

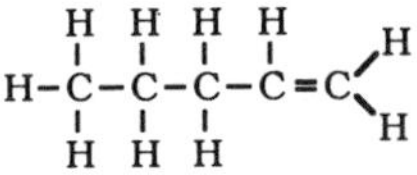

```
    H H H H      H
    | | | |     /
H - C-C-C-C = C
    | | |       \
    H H H        H
```

A.
```
    H     H
     \   /
   H  \ C /  H
    \  |  /
  H - C   C - H
   /       \
  H         H
      C - C
     /|   |\
    H H   H H
```

B.
```
 H           H H H
  \          | | |
   C=C - C - C - C - H
  /    |   | | |
 H     H   H H H
```

C.
```
    H H H H H
    | | | | |
H - C-C-C-C-C - H
    | | | | |
    H H H H H
```

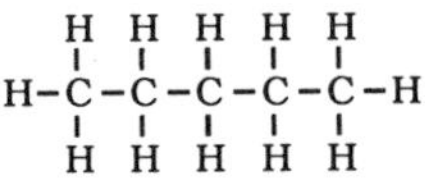

D.
```
    H H H H H
    | | | | |
H - C-C=C-C-C - H
    |     | |
    H     H H
```

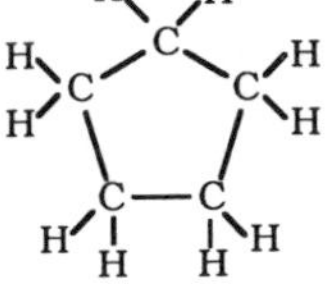

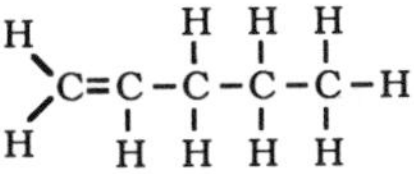

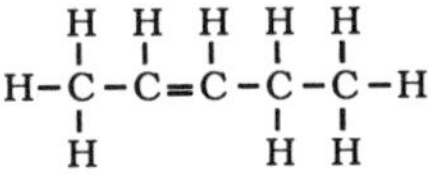

Questions 7 and 8 refer to isomers of alkenes with the formula C_5H_{10}.

A.

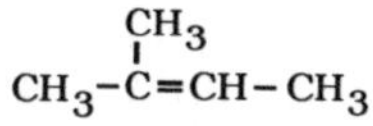

$$CH_3-\overset{\overset{\displaystyle CH_3}{|}}{C}=CH-CH_3$$

B.

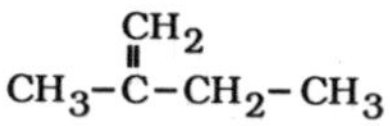

$$CH_3-\overset{\overset{\displaystyle CH_2}{\|}}{C}-CH_2-CH_3$$

C.

$$CH_2=\overset{\overset{\displaystyle CH_3}{|}}{C}-CH_2-CH_3$$

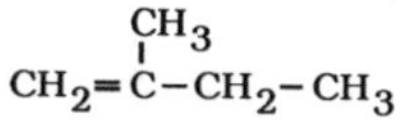

D.

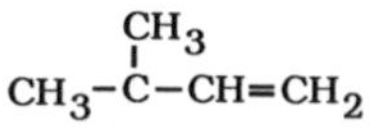

$$CH_3-\overset{\overset{\displaystyle CH_3}{|}}{C}-CH=CH_2$$

E.

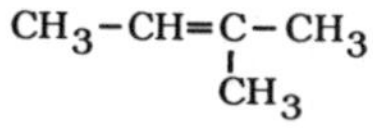

$$CH_3-CH=\overset{\underset{\displaystyle CH_3}{|}}{C}-CH_3$$

F.

$$CH_3-CH_2-\overset{\underset{\displaystyle CH_3}{|}}{C}=CH_2$$

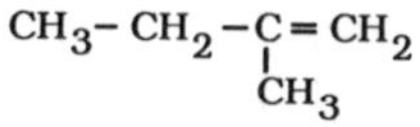

Pick out **all** the compounds that are **not** isomers of each of the structures.

7. **A**

8. **C**

In questions 9 to 12 decide whether each of the pairs of hydrocarbons are

A. are isomers

B. are **NOT** isomers.

9. 2-methlypentane   and   heptane

10. 2,3-dimethylbutane   and   hexane

11. pentane   and $CH_3CHCHCH_2CH_3$

12. hexane   and $CH_3CH(CH_3)CH(CH_3)CH_3$

In questions 1 to 6 decide whether each of the pairs of compounds

   A. are isomers   **B.** are **NOT** isomers.

1.
$$\begin{array}{ccc} & \text{H} & \text{H} \\ & | & | \\ \text{Br} - & \text{C} - & \text{C} - \text{Br} \\ & | & | \\ & \text{H} & \text{H} \end{array}$$
and
$$\begin{array}{ccc} & \text{H} & \text{Br} \\ & | & | \\ \text{H} - & \text{C} - & \text{C} - \text{H} \\ & | & | \\ & \text{Br} & \text{H} \end{array}$$

2.
$$\begin{array}{ccc} & \text{H} & \text{H} \\ & | & | \\ \text{Br} - & \text{C} - & \text{C} - \text{Br} \\ & | & | \\ & \text{H} & \text{H} \end{array}$$
and
$$\begin{array}{ccc} & \text{Br} & \text{H} \\ & | & | \\ \text{H} - & \text{C} - & \text{C} - \text{H} \\ & | & | \\ & \text{Br} & \text{H} \end{array}$$

3. $CH_3 - CH_2 - CH_2 - OH$ and
$$\begin{array}{c} \text{H} \\ | \\ CH_3 - \text{C} - CH_3 \\ | \\ \text{OH} \end{array}$$

4.
$$\begin{array}{c} \text{O} \\ \| \\ CH_3 - \text{C} - \text{O} - CH_3 \end{array}$$
and
$$\begin{array}{c} \text{O} \\ \| \\ CH_3 - CH_2 - \text{C} - \text{OH} \end{array}$$

5.
$$\begin{array}{c} \text{O} \\ \| \\ CH_3 - \text{C} - CH_3 \end{array}$$
and
$$\begin{array}{c} \text{O} \\ \| \\ CH_3 - CH_2 - \text{C} - \text{OH} \end{array}$$

6.
$$\begin{array}{c} \text{O} \\ \| \\ CH_3 - CH_2 - \text{C} - \text{H} \end{array}$$
and
$$\begin{array}{c} \text{O} \\ \| \\ CH_3 - \text{C} - CH_3 \end{array}$$

Questions 7 to 9 refer to the isomers of oxygen-containing compounds.

   A. CH_3COOCH_3 **B.** $CH_3CH_2CH_2COOH$
   C. CH_3COCH_3 **D.** $CH_3CH_2CH_2CHO$

7. Which compound is an isomer of propanoic acid?

8. Which compound is an isomer of propanal?

9. Which compound is an isomer of butanone?

In questions 10 to 15 decide whether each of the compounds

A. does have an isomeric form

B. does **NOT** have an isomeric form.

10. $CH_3CH_2CH_2OH$

11. C_2H_3Cl

12. chloroethane

13. C_3H_7Cl

14. CH_3CHCl_2

15. methanol

In questions 1 to 12 decide whether each of the molecules is

A. is able to undergo addition polymerisation

B. is **NOT** able to undergo addition polymerisation.

1. 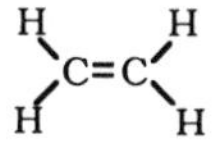
$$\underset{H}{\overset{H}{\diagdown}}C=C\underset{H}{\overset{H}{\diagup}}$$

2. 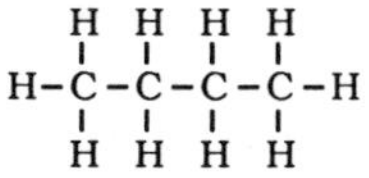
$$\underset{\overset{|}{H}\ \overset{|}{H}\ \overset{|}{H}\ \overset{|}{H}}{H-\overset{\overset{H}{|}}{C}-\overset{\overset{H}{|}}{C}-\overset{\overset{H}{|}}{C}-\overset{\overset{H}{|}}{C}-H}$$

3. 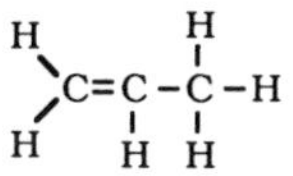
$$\underset{H}{\overset{H}{\diagdown}}C=\underset{\overset{|}{H}}{\overset{\overset{H}{|}}{C}}-\underset{\overset{|}{H}}{\overset{\overset{H}{|}}{C}}-H$$

4. 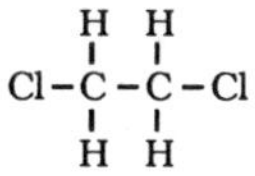
$$\underset{\overset{|}{H}\ \overset{|}{H}}{Cl-\overset{\overset{H}{|}}{C}-\overset{\overset{H}{|}}{C}-Cl}$$

5. ethane

6. propene

7. octane

8. styrene

9. C_3H_8

10. C_2F_4

11. $C_2H_4Br_2$

12. $CH_3CHCHCl$

In questions 13 to 25 decide whether each of the polymers is made by

A. addition polymerisation   **B.** condensation polymerisation.

13. polythene

14. polystyrene

15. bakelite

16. perspex

17. nylon

18. P.V.C.

19. formica

20. poly(butene)

21. $-CH_2-CH-CH_2-CH-CH_2-CH-$
$\qquad\quad CH_3 \qquad\quad CH_3 \qquad\quad CH_3$

22.

$$-\overset{O}{\overset{\|}{C}}-\overset{H}{\overset{|}{N}}-(CH_2)_6-\overset{H}{\overset{|}{N}}-\overset{O}{\overset{\|}{C}}-(CH_2)_4-\overset{O}{\overset{\|}{C}}-\overset{H}{\overset{|}{N}}-(CH_2)_6-\overset{H}{\overset{|}{N}}-\overset{O}{\overset{\|}{C}}-$$

23.

$$-\overset{F}{\underset{F}{\overset{|}{\underset{|}{C}}}}-\overset{F}{\underset{F}{\overset{|}{\underset{|}{C}}}}-\overset{F}{\underset{F}{\overset{|}{\underset{|}{C}}}}-\overset{F}{\underset{F}{\overset{|}{\underset{|}{C}}}}-\overset{F}{\underset{F}{\overset{|}{\underset{|}{C}}}}-\overset{F}{\underset{F}{\overset{|}{\underset{|}{C}}}}-$$

24. $-CH_2-CH-CH_2-CH-CH_2-CH-$
$\qquad\quad CN \qquad\qquad CN \qquad\qquad CN$

25.

$$-\overset{O}{\overset{\|}{C}}-O-(CH_2)_2-O-\overset{O}{\overset{\|}{C}}-(CH_2)_6-\overset{O}{\overset{\|}{C}}-O-(CH_2)_2-O-$$

Questions 26 to 29 refer to the part of the polymer shown.

26. How many repeating units are in the part of the polymer?

    A. 2   **B.** 3   **C.** 6   **D.** 9

27. What is the repeating unit?

    A.

    B.

    C.

    D.

28. What is the name of the monomer?

    A. ethene   **B.** propane   **C.** propene   **D.** butane

29. What is the name of the polymer?

    A. polythene   **B.** poly(propene)

    C. poly(butene)   **D.** P.V.C.

30. Polyvinyl chloride is a polymer of vinyl chloride, $CH_2 = CHCl$ (chloroethene).

    Which of the following is part of the formula for polyvinyl chloride?

    A.

    B.

    C.

    D.

31. Acrilan is an addition polymer of acrylonitrile. The structure of acrylonitrile is:

$$\underset{H}{\overset{H}{\diagdown}} C = C \underset{CN}{\overset{H}{\diagup}}$$

Which of the following is part of the structure for Acrilan?

A.

$$-\overset{\overset{H}{|}}{\underset{\underset{H}{|}}{C}}-\overset{\overset{H}{|}}{\underset{\underset{CN}{|}}{C}}-\overset{\overset{H}{|}}{\underset{\underset{H}{|}}{C}}-\overset{\overset{H}{|}}{\underset{\underset{CN}{|}}{C}}-$$

B.

$$-\overset{\overset{H}{|}}{\underset{\underset{CH_3}{|}}{C}}-\overset{\overset{H}{|}}{C}=N-\overset{\overset{H}{|}}{\underset{\underset{CH_3}{|}}{C}}-\overset{\overset{H}{|}}{C}=N-$$

C.

$$-\overset{\overset{CN}{|}}{C}=\overset{\overset{H}{|}}{\underset{\underset{CN}{|}}{C}}-\overset{\overset{CN}{|}}{C}=\overset{\overset{H}{|}}{\underset{\underset{CN}{|}}{C}}-$$

D.

$$=\overset{\overset{H}{|}}{C}-\overset{\overset{H}{|}}{\underset{\underset{H}{|}}{C}}-N=\overset{\overset{H}{|}}{C}-\overset{\overset{H}{|}}{\underset{\underset{H}{|}}{C}}-N=$$

32. Which monomer could polymerise to give the polymer shown?

$$-\overset{\overset{CH_3}{|}}{\underset{\underset{Cl}{|}}{C}}-\overset{\overset{H}{|}}{\underset{\underset{H}{|}}{C}}-\overset{\overset{CH_3}{|}}{\underset{\underset{Cl}{|}}{C}}-\overset{\overset{H}{|}}{\underset{\underset{H}{|}}{C}}-\overset{\overset{CH_3}{|}}{\underset{\underset{Cl}{|}}{C}}-\overset{\overset{H}{|}}{\underset{\underset{H}{|}}{C}}-$$

A.

$$\overset{\overset{H}{|}}{C}=\overset{\overset{H}{|}}{\underset{\underset{H}{|}}{C}}-\overset{\overset{H}{|}}{\underset{\underset{Cl}{|}}{C}}-CH_3$$

B.

$$CH_3-\overset{\overset{H}{|}}{C}=\overset{}{\underset{\underset{Cl}{|}}{C}}-CH_3$$

C.

$$CH_3-\overset{\overset{H}{|}}{C}=\overset{\overset{H}{|}}{\underset{\underset{Cl}{|}}{C}}$$

D.

$$CH_3-\overset{}{\underset{\underset{Cl}{|}}{C}}=\overset{\overset{H}{|}}{\underset{\underset{H}{|}}{C}}$$

33. Which monomer could polymerise to give the polymer shown?

$$-\overset{\overset{H}{|}}{\underset{\underset{H}{|}}{C}}-\overset{\overset{CH_3}{|}}{\underset{\underset{CN}{|}}{C}}-\overset{\overset{H}{|}}{\underset{\underset{H}{|}}{C}}-\overset{\overset{CH_3}{|}}{\underset{\underset{CN}{|}}{C}}-$$

A.

$$\underset{CN}{\overset{CH_3}{\diagdown}} C = C \underset{H}{\overset{CH_3}{\diagup}}$$

B.

$$\underset{CN}{\overset{H}{\diagdown}} C = C \underset{CH_3}{\overset{CH_3}{\diagup}}$$

C.

$$\underset{CN}{\overset{H}{\diagdown}} C = C \underset{H}{\overset{CH_3}{\diagup}}$$

D.

$$\underset{H}{\overset{H}{\diagdown}} C = C \underset{CN}{\overset{CH_3}{\diagup}}$$

Questions 34 and 35 refer to nylon. Part of the polymer chain is shown.

$$\underset{\substack{\|\\ O}}{-C}-(CH_2)_4-\underset{\substack{\|\\ O}}{C}-\underset{\substack{|\\ H}}{N}-(CH_2)_4-\underset{\substack{|\\ H}}{N}-\underset{\substack{\|\\ O}}{C}-(CH_2)_4-\underset{\substack{\|\\ O}}{C}-\underset{\substack{|\\ H}}{N}-(CH_2)_4-\underset{\substack{|\\ H}}{N}-$$

34. How many repeating units are in the part of the polymer shown?

   A. 1   **B.** 2   **C.** 3   **D.** 4

35. Which is (are) the monomers unit(s)?

   A.

   $$HO-\underset{\substack{\|\\ O}}{C}-(CH_2)_4-\underset{\substack{\|\\ O}}{C}-\underset{\substack{|\\ N}}{}-(CH_2)_4-\underset{\substack{|\\ H}}{N}-H$$

   B.

   $$HO-\underset{\substack{\|\\ O}}{C}-(CH_2)_4-\underset{\substack{|\\ H}}{N}-H$$

   C.

   $$HO-\underset{\substack{\|\\ O}}{C}-(CH_2)_4-\underset{\substack{\|\\ O}}{C}-OH \qquad H-\underset{\substack{|\\ N}}{}-(CH_2)_4-\underset{\substack{|\\ H}}{N}-H$$

   D.

   $$H-\underset{\substack{\|\\ O}}{C}-(CH_2)_4-\underset{\substack{\|\\ O}}{C}-H \qquad HO-\underset{\substack{|\\ N}}{}-(CH_2)_4-\underset{\substack{|\\ H}}{N}-OH$$

36. A condensation polymer is made from the monomer shown.

   $$H-\underset{\substack{|\\ H}}{N}-\underset{\substack{|\\ H}}{\overset{CH_3}{C}}-\underset{\substack{\|\\ O}}{C}-OH$$

   Which of the following is part of the polymer chain?

   A.

   $$-\underset{\substack{|\\ H}}{N}-\underset{\substack{|\\ H}}{\overset{CH_3}{C}}-\underset{\substack{|\\ }}{N}-\underset{\substack{\|\\ O}}{C}-\underset{\substack{|\\ H}}{\overset{CH_3}{C}}-\underset{\substack{\|\\ O}}{C}-$$

   B.

   $$-\underset{\substack{|\\ H}}{N}-\underset{\substack{|\\ OH}}{\overset{CH_3}{C}}-\underset{}{C}-\underset{\substack{|\\ H}}{N}-\underset{\substack{|\\ OH}}{\overset{CH_3}{C}}-C-$$

   C.

   $$-\underset{\substack{|\\ H}}{N}-\underset{\substack{|\\ H}}{\overset{CH_3}{C}}-\underset{\substack{\|\\ O}}{C}-\underset{\substack{|\\ H}}{N}-\underset{\substack{|\\ H}}{\overset{CH_3}{C}}-\underset{\substack{\|\\ O}}{C}-$$

   D.

   $$-\underset{\substack{|\\ H}}{N}-\underset{\substack{|\\ H}}{\overset{CH_3}{C}}-\underset{\substack{\|\\ O}}{C}-\underset{\substack{|\\ H}}{N}-\underset{\substack{|\\ H}}{\overset{CH_3}{C}}-\underset{\substack{\|\\ O}}{C}-$$

Test 2.7   Cracking of hydrocarbons

Questions 1 to 17 refer to the experiment shown.

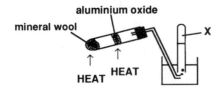

In the apparatus, the mineral wool was soaked with a liquid alkane, $C_{12}H_{26}$. Its vapour was passed over hot aluminium oxide and a gas collected at **X** by displacement of water.

Decide whether each of the statements is

A. TRUE   **B.** FALSE.

1. An addition reaction is taking place.

2. The aluminium oxide is changed to aluminium.

3. The gas collected is insoluble in water.

4. The aluminium oxide acts as a catalyst.

5. The gas collected burns to give both water and carbon dioxide.

6. Only methane gas is produced.

7. The aluminium oxide gradually melts.

8. The gas collected quickly decolourises bromine.

9. There is no change in the chemical composition of the aluminium oxide.

10. The gas collected could contain ethene.

11. The gas collected turns lime water milky.

12. The gas collected burns to give only water.

13. The gas collected contains a mixture of hydrocarbons.

14. The gas collected burns to give only carbon dioxide.

15. The gas collected contains unsaturated molecules.

16. Molecules with the formula $C_{13}H_{26}$ are found in the gas.

17. The gas collected could contain ethane.

18. A liquid hydrocarbon had no visible effect on bromine, but when it was cracked the gases produced decolourised bromine.

This is because

A. gases decolourise bromine; liquids do not

B. the gases formed were unsaturated; the liquid was not

C. the gases formed were at a higher temperature than the liquid

D. some of the gases formed by the cracking were not hydrocarbons.

19. $C_{16}H_{34}$ → $C_{10}H_{20}$ + **X**

What is the formula for **X**?

A. C_6H_{14} B. $C_{10}H_{22}$ C. $C_{16}H_{34}$ D. $C_{26}H_{54}$

20. $C_{10}H_{22}$ → C_6H_{12} + C_2H_6 + **X**

X must be

A. methane B. ethene C. butane D. butene.

21. Hexane can be cracked to give ethene and another hydrocarbon.

The other hydrocarbon must be

A. propane B. propene C. butane D. butene.

22. A C_{11} alkane is cracked into pentane and two other straight-chain hydrocarbons.

If one of these is ethene, the other must be

A. propane B. propene C. butane D. butene.

In questions 23 to 29 decide whether each of the statements is

A. TRUE B. FALSE.

23. Ethene and propene can be obtained by the cracking of naphtha.

24. Ethene can be obtained by the cracking of ethane.

25. Propene can be obtained by the cracking of ethane.

26. Propane can be obtained by the cracking of propene.

27. Branched chain alkanes can be obtained by the cracking of propane.

28. Hexene can be obtained by the cracking of ethene.

29. Ethene can be obtained by the cracking of propane.

Test 2.8   Structures of oxygen-containing organic compounds

The questions in this test refer to oxygen-containing organic compounds.

A.
$$CH_3-\overset{\overset{\displaystyle O}{\|}}{C}-CH_3$$

B. CH_3COOH

C. CH_3OH

D. butanone

E.
$$CH_3-O-\overset{\overset{\displaystyle O}{\|}}{C}-H$$

F. ethanal

G. CH_3-O-CH_3

H.
$$H-\overset{\nearrow O}{\underset{\searrow OH}{C}}$$

I.
$$CH_3-CH_2-\overset{\overset{\displaystyle O}{\|}}{C}-H$$

J. $CH_3COCH_2CH_3$

K.
$$CH_3-O-\overset{\overset{\displaystyle O}{\|}}{C}-CH_3$$

L. methanol

M. CH_3-O-CH_3

N. $HCOOCH_2CH_3$

O. CH_3CH_2CHO

P.
$$\overset{O}{\underset{}{\|}}$$
phenyl$-\overset{\overset{\displaystyle O}{\|}}{C}-CH_3$

Q. $CH_3-O-CH_2CH_3$

R.
$$\overset{O}{\|}\\ C\\ CH_2 \quad CH_2\\ CH_2-CH_2$$

S.
phenyl$-\overset{\overset{\displaystyle O}{\|}}{C}-O-CH_3$

T.
phenyl$-CHO$

U. $CH_3CH(OH)CH_3$

1. Pick out **all** the compounds which are **alcohols**.
2. Pick out **all** the compounds which are **organic acids**.
3. Pick out **all** the compounds which are **aldehydes**.
4. Pick out **all** the compounds which are **ketones**.

The questions in this test refer to alcohols.

A.

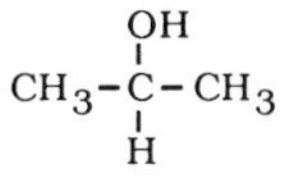

$$CH_3 - \underset{\underset{H}{|}}{\overset{\overset{OH}{|}}{C}} - CH_3$$

B.

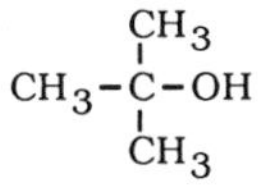

$$CH_3 - \underset{\underset{CH_3}{|}}{\overset{\overset{CH_3}{|}}{C}} - OH$$

C. $CH_3 - OH$

D.

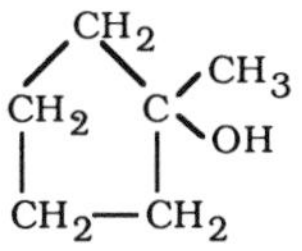

E.

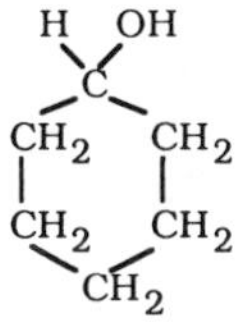

F.

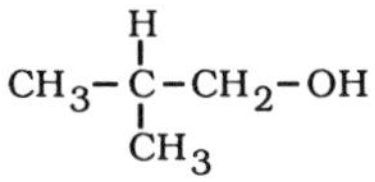

$$CH_3 - \underset{\underset{CH_3}{|}}{\overset{\overset{H}{|}}{C}} - CH_2 - OH$$

G.

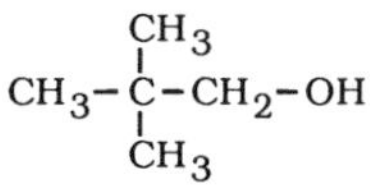

$$CH_3 - \underset{\underset{CH_3}{|}}{\overset{\overset{CH_3}{|}}{C}} - CH_2 - OH$$

H.

$$CH_3 - \underset{\underset{CH_3}{|}}{\overset{\overset{CH_3}{|}}{C}} \, - \, \underset{\underset{CH_3}{|}}{\overset{\overset{H}{|}}{C}} - OH$$

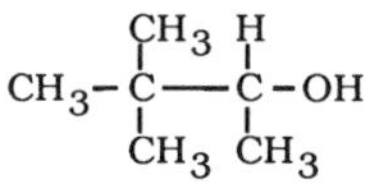

I. $CH_3CH(OH)CH_2CH_3$

J. $CH_3CH_2C(CH_3)_2OH$

K. $CH_3CH(CH_3)CH(CH_3)OH$

L. ethanol

M. hexan-2-ol

N. 2-methylbutan-1-ol

O. 3-methylpentan-2-ol

P. 3-methylhexan-3-ol

1. Pick out **all** the alcohols which are **primary** alcohols.

2. Pick out **all** the alcohols which are **secondary** alcohols.

3. Pick out **all** the alcohols which are **tertiary** alcohols.

Test 2.10   Oxidation

In questions 1 to 16 decide whether each of the alcohols can be oxidised to

A. an alkanal   **B.** an alkanone   **C.** neither.

1. CH_3-CH_2-OH

2. $CH_3-\underset{\underset{OH}{|}}{CH}-CH_3$

3. $CH_3-\underset{\underset{CH_3}{|}}{CH}-CH_2-OH$

4. $CH_3-\underset{\underset{CH_3}{|}}{\overset{\overset{CH_3}{|}}{C}}-OH$

5. $CH_3-\underset{\underset{CH_3}{|}}{\overset{\overset{CH_3}{|}}{C}}-CH_2-OH$

6.

7. $CH_3CH_2C(CH_3)_2OH$

8. $CH_3CH(CH_3)CH(CH_3)OH$

9. $CH_3CH_2C(CH_3)_2CH_2OH$

10. $CH_3CH(OH)CH_2CH_3$

11. propan-1-ol

12. pentan-3-ol

13. 3-methylpentan-3-ol

14. 2-methylpentan-3-ol

15. 2-methylhexan-1-ol

16. cycloheptanol

In questions 17 to 24 decide whether each of the carbonyl compounds

A. can be easily oxidised to an alkanoic acid.

B. can **NOT** be easily oxidised to an alkanoic acid.

17. ethanal

18. propanone

19. pentanal

20. hexan-2-one

21. $H-\underset{\underset{H}{|}}{C}=O$

22. $CH_3-CH_2-\underset{\underset{O}{||}}{C}-CH_3$

23. $CH_3-CH_2-\underset{\underset{H}{|}}{C}=O$

24. $CH_3-CH_2-\underset{\underset{O}{||}}{C}-CH_2-CH_3$

Test 2.11   Reactions of oxygen-containing organic compounds

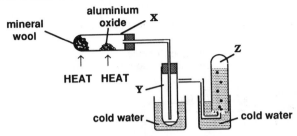

The mineral wool was soaked with an alcohol. The vapour was passed over red-hot aluminium oxide.

1. The reaction taking place in tube **X** is an example of

    A. condensation   **B.** dehydration

    C. dehydrogenation   **D.** reduction.

2. What is the product when ethanol is used in the reaction?

    A. ethane   **B.** ethene

    C. ethanal   **D.** ethanoic acid

3. Any traces of gas **Z** dissolved in the liquid in **Y** are removed.

    What effect would bromine solution have on the purified liquid in **Y** and on the gas in **Z**?

    A. Both **Y** and **Z** would react.

    B. **Z** would react and **Y** would not.

    C. **Y** would react and **Z** would not.

    D. Neither **Y** nor **Z** would react.

4. What is the product when butan-1-ol is used in the reaction?

    A. but-1-ene   **B.** but-2-ene

    C. a mixture of but-1-ene and but-2-ene

5. What is the product when butan-2-ol is used in the reaction?

    A. but-1-ene   **B.** but-2-ene

    C. a mixture of but-1-ene and but-2-ene

6. What alcohol will produce pent-2-ene as the only product?

   A. pentan-1-ol   **B.** pentan-2-ol
   C. pentan-3-ol

Questions 7 to 12 refer to the experiment shown.

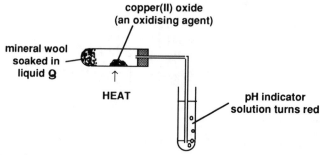

Decide whether each of the following liquids

   A. could be liquid Q   **B.** could **NOT** be liquid Q.

7. propanone

8. paraffin

9. propanal

10. pentane

11. propan-1-ol

12. propan-2-ol

Questions 13 to 15 refer to the oxidation of carbonyl compounds.

   A. propanone   **B.** butanal
   C. butanone   **D.** propanal

13. What compound is formed by the oxidation of butan-2-ol?

14. What compound is oxidised to produce $CH_3CH_2CH_2COOH$?

15. What compound is formed by the oxidation of $CH_3CH_2CH_2OH$?

16. When the vapour of a liquid **X** is passed over heated copper(II) oxide (an oxidising agent), a reaction occurs and the vapour produced gives an orange precipitate with Benedict's (or Fehling's) solution.

Which of the following could be **X**?

A. propan-1-ol
B. propan-2-ol
C. propanal
D. propanone

Questions 17 and 18 refer to types of reaction.

A. condensation   B. oxidation
C. hydrolysis   D. dehydration

17. What type of reaction takes place when methanol is converted to methanal?

18. What type of reaction takes place when butanol is converted to butene?

19. Propan-1-ol is converted to propanal by warming it with potassium dichromate solution acidified with sulphuric acid.

The function of the acid/dichromate mixture is to

A. reduce the alcohol
B. dehydrate the alcohol
C. act as a catalyst
D. oxidise the alcohol.

Test 2.12   Ethanol and ethanoic acid

Decide whether each of the statements is

A. TRUE   **B.** FALSE.

1. Alcoholic drinks can be made from fruit or vegetables.

2. Oxygen gas is produced in the making of ethanol from carbohydrates.

3. Ethanol is produced from carbohydrates by an addition reaction.

4. Oxygen gas is used up in the making of ethanol from carbohydrates.

5. Distillation is a method of increasing the alcohol concentration in alcoholic drinks.

6. Fermentation is a way of separating alcohol and water.

7. Ethanol is the name of the alcohol in alcoholic drinks.

8. An enzyme in yeast is required for fermentation.

9. Carbon dioxide gas is produced in the making of ethanol from carbohydrates.

10. Glucose can be used to make alcohol.

11. Fermentation is a way of separating liquids due to differences in boiling points.

12. Alcoholic drinks are prepared by the fermentation of carbohydrate.

13. Ethanol reacts with the nitrogen of the air to form an acid.

14. Vinegar is a solution of ethanoic acid in water.

15. Ethanoic acid can be prepared from poor quality wines and beers.

16. Ethanoic acid can be produced by the oxidation of naphtha.

17. Naphtha reacts with hydrogen to produce ethanoic acid.

18. Direct catalytic hydration of ethene is an industrial way of making ethanol.

19. Ethanol can be made by the reaction of water with ethane.

20. The oxidation of ethene is an industrial route to ethanol.

Test 2.13

Organic reactions

The questions in this test refer to types of reaction.

A. addition	**B.** hydration	**C.** condensation
D. oxidation	**E.** cracking	**F.** polymerisation
G. dehydration		

What type of reaction is each of the following?

(Note that for some for some of the questions more than one response may be correct.)

1. ethene $\rightarrow$ ethane

2. propane $\rightarrow$ propene

3. methanol $\rightarrow$ methanal

4. propene $\rightarrow$ propanol

5. propene $\rightarrow$ poly(propene)

6. butan-2-ol $\rightarrow$ butanone

7. propan-2-ol $\rightarrow$ propene

8. ethanal $\rightarrow$ ethanoic acid

9. a diol + a diamine $\rightarrow$ a polyamide

10. $CH_3CH(OH)CH_3$ $\rightarrow$ CH_3COCH_3

11. CH_3CHCH_2 $\rightarrow$ $CH_3CHClCH_2Cl$

12. CH_3CH_2OH $\rightarrow$ CH_3CHO

13. CH_2CH_2 $\rightarrow$ CH_2CH_2

14. CH_3CH_2OH $\rightarrow$ CH_2CH_2

15. HCHO $\rightarrow$ HCOOH

16. $H_2N-\boxed{\text{III}}-N_2H$ $HOOC-\boxed{\equiv}-COOH$ $\rightarrow$ $-NH-\boxed{\text{III}}-NHCO-\boxed{\equiv}-CO-$

17. CH_3CH_3 $\rightarrow$ CH_2CH_2

18. CH_2CH_2 $\rightarrow$ CH_3CH_2OH

Test 2.14   Aromatic hydrocarbons

In questions 1 to 5 decide whether each of the statements about aromatic hydrocarbons is

A. TRUE   **B.** FALSE.

1. Aromatic hydrocarbons can be obtained from the naphtha fraction of oil.

2. Aromatic hydrocarbons can be obtained by the polymerisation of ethene.

3. Aromatic hydrocarbons can be obtained from coal.

4. Aromatic hydrocarbons can be obtained by the cracking of hexane.

5. Aromatic hydrocarbons are important feedstocks.

In questions 6 to 13 decide whether each of the statements about benzene is

A. TRUE   **B.** FALSE.

6. Benzene contains more elements than hexane.

7. Benzene has the formula C_6H_6.

8. Benzene is more volatile than ethane.

9. Benzene undergoes addition reactions more readily than hexene.

10. Benzene has the same empirical formula as ethene.

11. Benzene behaves towards bromine water as if unsaturated.

12. Benzene does **not** react readily with a solution of bromine.

13. Benzene is an isomer of cyclohexane.

14. All the carbon to carbon bonds are the same length.

15. Only one product is formed when a hydrogen atom is replaced by a chlorine atom.

16. More than one product is formed when two hydrogen atoms are replaced by two chlorine atoms.

Test 2.15   Fuels

In questions 1 to 4 decide whether each of the following

A. can be used directly as a fuel

B. can **NOT** be used directly as a fuel.

1. coal   3. natural gas

2. crude oil   4. petrol

In questions 5 to 8 decide whether each of the molecules

A. is likely to be found in natural gas

B. is **NOT** likely to be found in natural gas.

5. C_2H_6 7. C_5H_{12}

6. $C_{10}H_{22}$ 8. CH_4

In questions 9 to 12 decide whether each of the hydrocarbons

A. is likely to be found in liquified petroleum gas

B. is **NOT** likely to be found in liquified petroleum gas.

9. methane   11. propane

10. octane   12. butane

13. Which molecule is most likely to be found in liquid petroleum gas?

    A. CH_4 **B.** C_3H_8 **C.** C_8H_{18} **D.** $C_{18}H_{38}$

14. The refining of crude oil depends on the fact that the different hydrocarbons have different

    A. ignition temperatures   **B.** solubilities

    C. boiling points   **D.** densities.

Questions 15 to 21 refer to properties of fractions, collected over the temperature ranges shown.

Fraction	Temperature range / °C
1	less than 40
2	40 - 75
3	150-240
4	220-250
5	250-350
6	>350

Decide whether each of the statements about the fractions is

A. TRUE   **B.** FALSE.

15. Fraction 3 is more viscous than fraction 6.

16. Fraction 2 is more volatile than fraction 4.

17. Fraction 3 is less flammable than fraction 6.

18. Fraction 5 is thicker than fraction 3.

19. Fraction 1 has a higher boiling point than fraction 4.

20. Fraction 2 burns more easily than fraction 5.

21. Fraction 3 boils at a lower temperature than fraction 5.

Questions 22 to 24 are about the uses of the products of fractional distillation of crude oil.

A. diesel   **B.** bitumen
C. kerosene   **D.** lubricating oil

22. Which product is used to tar roads?

23. Which product is used as a fuel for jet aeroplanes?

24. Which product is used to reduce friction and wear in car engines?

Test 2.16   Petrol and diesel

In questions 1 to 10 decide whether each of the statements is

A. TRUE   **B.** FALSE.

1. Diesel evaporates more readily than petrol.

2. Diesel contains smaller molecules than petrol.

3. Diesel is produced by blending different gas oil fractions obtained by distillation.

4. The addition of lead improves the efficiency of petrol fuels.

5. Diesel contains more branched chain alkanes and aromatic hydrocarbons than petrol.

6. Reforming of naphtha produces aromatic hydocarbons for use in petrol.

7. An electric spark is used to ignite petrol in a petrol engine.

8. Leaded petrol contains more aromatic hydrocarbons and branched chain alkanes than unleaded petrol.

9. An electric spark is used to ignite diesel in a diesel engine.

10. Distillation of naphtha leads to the production of branched chain alkanes from straight chain alkanes.

Questions 11 and 12 refer to molecules found in fuels.

A. CH_4 **B.** C_3H_8 **C.** C_8H_{18} **D.** $C_{20}H_{42}$

11. Which molecule is most likely to be found in petrol?

12. Which molecule is most likely to be found in diesel?

In questions 13 to 18 decide whether each of the gases found in car exhausts

A. is a result of incomplete combustion
B. is **NOT** a result of incomplete combustion.

13. octane   16. carbon monoxide

14. nitrogen dioxide   17. water vapour

15. carbon dioxide   18. sulphur dioxide

Test 2.17   Synthesis gas

In questions 1 to 4 decide whether each of the following

A. is used to produce synthesis gas

B. is **NOT** used to produce synthesis gas.

1. petrol   3. crude oil

2. coal   4. methane

5. Which of the following processes is used to produce synthesis gas?

    A. steam reforming   **B.** fractional distillation

    C. catalytic cracking   **D.** direct oxidation

6. Synthesis gas can be made by

    A. fractional distillation of liquid air

    B. burning coal in excess air

    C. burning natural gas in a limited supply of air

    D. reacting natural gas with steam.

In questions 7 to 12 decide whether each of the gases

A. is a component of synthesis gas

B. is **NOT** a component of synthesis gas.

7. carbon dioxide   10. nitrogen

8. oxygen   11. carbon monoxide

9. hydrogen   12. sulphur dioxide

13. Which of the following is directly made from synthesis gas?

    A. ethanol   **B.** ethene   **C.** methanol   **D.** methane

14. Methanal can be produced from methanol by

    A. cracking   **B.** addition   **C.** reforming   **D.** oxidation.

15. Thermosetting plastics are produced from methanal by

    A. catalytic cracking   **B.** condensation polymerisation

    C. steam reforming   **D.** fractional distillation.

Test 3.1   The mole (i)

1. What is the mass, in grams, of 0.25 mol of carbon dioxide?

   A. 7   **B.** 11   **C.** 15   **D.** 19

2. How many moles are contained in 5 g sodium hydroxide?

   A. 0.1   **B.** 0.125   **C.** 0.25   **D.** 0.5

3. How many moles of sodium hydroxide must be dissolved to make 200 cm^3 of 2 mol l^{-1} solution?

   A. 0.02   **B.** 0.04   **C.** 0.2   **D.** 0.4

4. What is the concentration, in mol l^{-1}, of a solution which contains 0.5 mol of hydrogen chloride dissolved in 200 cm^3 of solution?

   A. 0.2   **B.** 0.5   **C.** 1.0   **D.** 2.5

5. What volume of a 0.2 mol l^{-1} solution contains 1 mol?

   A. 200 cm^3 **B.** 500 cm^3 **C.** 1 litre   **D.** 5 litres

6. What mass of sodium carbonate, in grams, is required to make 50 cm^3 of 0.1 mol l^{-1} solution?

   A. 0.53   **B.** 1.06   **C.** 5.3   **D.** 10.6

7. What is the concentration of a solution, in mol l^{-1}, containing 4 g of sodium hydroxide in 100 cm^3 of water?

   A. 0.01   **B.** 0.4   **C.** 1   **D.** 4

8. 0.5 mol of copper(II) chloride and 0.5 mol of copper(II) sulphate are dissolved in water and made up to 500 cm^3 of solution.

   What is the concentration, in mol l^{-1}, of Cu^{2+} (aq) ions in the solution ?

   A. 0.5   **B.** 1.0   **C.** 2.0   **D.** 4.0

9. A mixture of magnesium chloride and magnesium sulphate is known to contain 0.6 mol of chloride ion and 0.2 mol of sulphate ion.

How many moles of magnesium ions are present?

A. 0.4   **B.** 0.5   **C.** 0.8   **D.** 1.0

10. A mixture of sodium chloride and sodium sulphate is known to contain 0.5 mol of sodium ions and 0.2 mol of chloride ions.

How many moles of sulphate ions are present?

A. 0.15   **B.** 0.20   **C.** 0.25   **D.** 0.30

11. A mixture of sodium chloride and sodium sulphate is known to contain 0.6 mol of chloride ion and 0.2 mol of sulphate ion.

How many moles of sodium ions are present?

A. 0.4   **B.** 0.5   **C.** 0.8   **D.** 1.0

12. A mixture of magnesium bromide and magnesium sulphate is known to contain 3 mol of magnesium and 4 mol of bromide ions.

How many moles of sulphate ions are present?

A. 1   **B.** 2   **C.** 3   **D.** 4

13. A mixture of sodium sulphate and copper(II) sulphate is known to contain 3 mol of sulphate ions and 1 mol of copper ions.

How many moles of sodium ions are present?

A. 1   **B.** 2   **C.** 3   **D.** 4

Test 3.2

The mole (ii)

1. Which solid contains the greatest number of atoms?

    A. 20 g of carbon   **B.** 20 g of calcium
    C. 20 g of magnesium   **D.** 20 g of sulphur

2. Which gas contains the smallest number of molecules?

    A. 100 g of fluorine   **B.** 100 g of nitrogen
    C. 100 g of oxygen   **D.** 100 g of hydrogen

3. Which gas contains the greatest number of molecules?

    A. 0.10 g of hydrogen gas   **B.** 0.17 g of ammonia gas
    C. 0.32 g of methane gas   **D.** 0.35 g of chlorine gas

4. Which gas contains the greatest number of atoms?

    A. 1 g hydrogen   **B.** 32 g oxygen
    C. 20 g neon   **D.** 40 g argon

5. 96 g of magnesium contains twice as many atoms as

    A. 207 g of lead   **B.** 2 mol of oxygen molecules
    C. 2 mol of calcium   **D.** 48 g of carbon.

6. Which of the following contains the greatest number of atoms?

    A. 12 g carbon   **B.** 9 g hydrogen oxide
    C. 16 g oxygen   **D.** 14 g carbon monoxide

7. Which of the following contains the smallest number of hydrogen atoms?

    A. 17 g of ammonia (NH_3) **B.** 16 g of methane (CH_4)
    C. 36 g of water (H_2O) **D.** 14 g of ethene (C_2H_4)

8. 4 g of sodium hydroxide contains the same number of ions as

    A. 17 g sodium nitrate   **B.** 10 g calcium carbonate
    C. 14.2 g sodium sulphate   **D.** 5.8 g magnesium hydroxide.

9. What is the amount, in moles, of oxygen atoms in 0.5 mol of carbon dioxide?

   A. 0.25   **B.** 0.5   **C.** 1   **D.** 2

10. One mole of calcium chloride contains

    A. 3 mol of atoms   **C.** 1 mol of positive ions
    B. 1 mol of molecules   **D.** 1 mol of negative ions.

11. 36 g of hydrogen oxide contains

    A. 2 mol of hydrogen atoms
    B. 1 mol of atoms
    C. 4 mol of hydrogen atoms
    D. 2 mol of atoms.

12. The molecular formula for a gas is X_3.
    How many X atoms will be present in 0.25 mol of X?

    A. $0.5 \times 6 \times 10^{23}$ **B.** $0.75 \times 6 \times 10^{23}$
    C. $1 \times 6 \times 10^{23}$ **D.** $3 \times 6 \times 10^{23}$

13. How many atoms are in 20 g of calcium?

    A. 1×10^{23} **B.** 3×10^{23} **C.** 6×10^{23} **D.** 1.2×10^{24}

14. How many molecules are in 3.2 g of methane (CH_4)?

    A. 1×10^{23} **B.** 1.2×10^{23} **C.** 6×10^{23} **D.** 3×10^{24}

15. How many atoms are in 0.5 mol of gaseous flourine?

    A. 1.5×10^{23} **B.** 3×10^{23} **C.** 6×10^{23} **D.** 1.2×10^{24}

16. How many atoms are in 0.44 g of carbon dioxide?

    A. 1.8×10^{22} **B.** 6×10^{22} **C.** 1.2×10^{23} **D.** 0.8×10^{23}

17. How many ions are in 20 g of sodium hydroxide?

    A. 3×10^{22} **B.** 6×10^{22} **C.** 3×10^{23} **D.** 6×10^{23}

18. What is the mass, in grams, of one sodium atom?

    A. 6×10^{23} **B.** 6×10^{-23}

    C. 3.8×10^{-23} **D.** 3.8×10^{-24}

19. What is the mass, in grams, of 100 molecules of hydrogen?

    A. 6×10^{23} **B.** 1.66×10^{-22}

    C. 3.33×10^{-22} **D.** 1.2×10^{-23}

20. How many protons are in 120 g of carbon?

    A. 60   **B.** 1×10^{24} **C.** 6×10^{24} **D.** 3.6×10^{25}

21. How many electrons are in 1.2 g of magnesium ions?

    A. 3×10^{22} **B.** 3.6×10^{22} **C.** 3.6×10^{23} **D.** 6×10^{24}

Test 3.3   Electrolysis

Questions 1 to 5 refer to the amounts of substances produced during electrolysis.

Decide whether each of the amounts

A. is produced by passage of 96 500 coulombs of electricity

B. is **NOT** produced by passage of 96 500 coulombs of electricity.

1. 1 mol of zinc

2. 0.5 mol of magnesium

3. 2 mol of sodium

4. 1 mol of hydrogen

5. 0.5 mol of iodine

Questions 6 to 10 refer to the quantities of electricity, in coulombs, used during electrolysis.

A.	0.5 x 96 500	**B.**	1 x 96 500
C.	1.5 x 96 500	**D.**	2 x 96 500

What is the quantity of electricity required to produce each of the amounts?

6. 0.5 mol of potassium

7. 1 mol of nickel

8. 0.5 mol of chlorine

9. 0.5 mol of aluminium

10. 0.25 mol oxygen

11. If a steady current of 0.4 A was passed through silver nitrate solution, concentration 1 mol l^{-1}, for 40 minutes, approximately how many moles of silver would be liberated?

    A. 0.001   **B.** 0.01   **C.** 0.1   **D.** 1

12. In the electrolysis of a solution of copper(II) sulphate using copper electrodes, the passage of 96 500 C of electricity results in the negative electrode

A.	gaining 64 g mass	**B.**	gaining 32 g mass
C.	losing 64 g mass	**D.**	losing 32 g mass.

13. The unlabelled line on the graph was obtained by plotting the mass of copper metal deposited against charge passed during the electrolysis of a solution of copper(I) chloride.

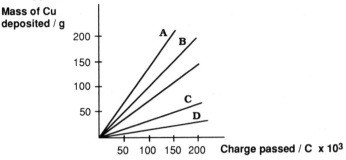

If a solution of copper(II) chloride was electrolysed, which line would be obtained?

14. Silver nitrate solution, concentration 1 mol l^{-1}, is electrolysed. A steady current is maintained until 1.08 g of silver is formed on electrode **R**. The time required to deposit the silver is 30 minutes.

What would be the approximate reading, in amps, on the ammeter?

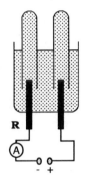

A. 0.5
B. 1.5
C. 2.0
D. 2.5

Questions 15 and 16 refer to the experiment shown. The metals Ag and '**M**' are deposited by electrolysis.

15. It took 54 hours to deposit 1 mol of Ag.

How long would it take to deposit 1 mol of **M**?

A. 54 **n** hours   **B.** 54 hours
C. 54 / **n** hours   **D.** You cannot say without the relative atomic masses of Ag and **M**.

16. It took 30 minutes to deposit 1 g of Ag.

How long would it take to deposit 1 g of **M**?

A. 30 minutes   **B.** 30 **n** minutes
C. 30 / **n** minutes   **D.** You cannot say without the relative atomic masses of Ag and **M**.

Test 3.4 The mole (iii)

For the questions in this test assume that all measurements are made at the same temperature and pressure.

1. Which gas has the smallest volume?

   A. 10 g of oxygen   **B.** 10 g of carbon monoxide
   C. 10 g of ethane (C_2H_6) **D.** 10 g of hydrogen

2. Which gas has the greatest volume?

   A. 1 g of hydrogen   **B.** 14 g of nitrogen
   C. 20 g of neon   **D.** 35.5 g of chlorine

3. Which gas has the same volume as 1 g of helium?

   A. 1.6 g of methane   **B.** 2.2 g of carbon dioxide
   C. 3.6 g of hydrogen oxide   **D.** 16 g of sulphur dioxide

4. Given equal volumes of each gas, in which pair do both gases have the same mass?

   A. hydrogen and helium   **B.** methane and oxygen
   C. ethene and nitrogen   **D.** carbon monoxide and nitrogen monoxide

5. Which gas has the highest density?

   A. CO   **B.** NO   **C.** N_2 **D.** C_2H_4

6. The volume of 1 g of hydrogen is 11.4 litres.

   What is the volume, in litres, of 2 mol of hydrogen?

   A. 5.7   **B.** 11.4
   C. 22.8   **D.** 45.6

7. A gaseous hydrocarbon has a density of 1.25 g l^{-1}. The molar volume of the gas is 22.2 litres.

   What is the molecular formula?

   A. CH_4 **B.** C_2H_4
   C. C_3H_6 **D.** C_4H_8

In questions 8 to 10 take the molar volume to be 23 litres mol^{-1}.

8. What is the volume, in litres, of 2 g of neon?

   A. 1   **B.** 2   **C.** 2.3   **D.** 23

9. How many molecules are in 2.3 litres of oxygen?

   A. 6×10^{22} **B.** 1.2×10^{23} **C.** 6×10^{23} **D.** 1.2×10^{24}

10. How many atoms are in 0.23 litres of hydrogen?

    A. 6×10^{21} **B.** 1.2×10^{22} **C.** 6×10^{22} **D.** 1.2×10^{23}

Test 3.5

The mole (iv)

For the questions in this test decide whether each of the statements is

A. TRUE   **B.** FALSE.

The Avogadro Constant is the same as the number of

1. atoms in 24 g of carbon

2. atoms in 0.5 mol of chlorine molecules

3. molecules in 0.5 mol of carbon monoxide

4. molecules in 16 g of oxygen

5. molecules in 2 g of hydrogen

6. ions in 1 litre of sodium chloride solution, concentration 1 mol l^{-1}

7. ions in 0.5 mol of sodium oxide

8. electrons in 0.5 mol of helium atoms

9. protons in 2 g of sulphur.

Questions 10 to 13 refer to 16 g of oxygen, 2 g of hydrogen and 71 g of chlorine.

10. Each occupies the same volume.

11. Each contains 6 x 10^{23} atoms.

12. Each contains 6 x 10^{23} molecules.

13. Each may be liberated by 2 x 96 500 coulombs of electricity.

Questions 14 to 17 refer to carbon dioxide gas.

14. The mass of 6 x 10^{23} molecules is 44 g.

15. One molecule is 44 times as heavy as a molecule of hydrogen.

16. 44 g occupy the same volume as 32 g oxygen.

17. 44 g of the gas contains the same number of atoms as 20 g of neon.

18. 44 g of the gas contains 6 x 10^{23} carbon atoms

19. 44 g of the gas contains the same number of molecules as 1 g of hydrogen.

Questions 20 to 25 refer to the Avogadro Constant.

20. 64 g of sulphur contains 6×10^{23} atoms.

21. 1 g of hydrogen contains 6×10^{23} molecules.

22. 500 cm^3 of 2 mol l^{-1} sodium hydroxide solution contains 6×10^{23} sodium ions.

23. 6 g of water contains 6×10^{23} atoms.

24. 64 g of sulphur dioxide contains 6×10^{23} atoms.

25. 1 litre of 1 mol l^{-1} sulphuric acid contains 6×10^{23} sulphate ions.

Test 3.6   Calculations based on equations (i)

1. $2CO_{(g)}$ + $O_{2(g)}$ → $2CO_{2(g)}$

   What mass, in grams, of carbon dioxide would be obtained by the combustion of 28 g carbon monoxide?

   A. 28   **B.** 44   **C.** 56   **D.** 88

2. $CH_{4(g)}$ + $2O_{2(g)}$ → $CO_{2(g)}$ + $2H_2O_{(l)}$

   What mass, in grams, of methane is required to produce 1.8 g of water?

   A. 0.8   **B.** 1.6   **C.** 8.0   **D.** 16.0

   Questions 3 to 8 refer to the neutralisation of 20 cm^3 of sodium hydroxide solution, concentration 0.2 mol l^{-1}, by acids.

   Decide whether each of the acids

   A. can neutralise the alkali to form a neutral solution
   B. can **NOT** neutralise the alkali to form a neutral solution.

3. 20 cm^3 hydrochloric acid, concentration 0.2 mol l^{-1}

4. 40 cm^3 hydrochloric acid, concentration 0.1 mol l^{-1}

5. 10 cm^3 hydrochloric acid, concentration 0.2 mol l^{-1}

6. 20 cm^3 sulphuric acid, concentration 0.2 mol l^{-1}

7. 20 cm^3 sulphuric acid , concentration 0.1 mol l^{-1}

8. 10 cm^3 sulphuric acid, concentration 0.2 mol l^{-1}

9. 50 cm^3 of sulphuric acid, concentration, 2 mol l^{-1}, required 100 cm^3 of sodium hydroxide solution for complete neutralisation.

   What was the concentration, in mol l^{-1}, of the sodium hydroxide solution ?

   A. 0.25   **B.** 0.5   **C.** 1   **D.** 2

10. When 2 g hydrogen is exploded in excess oxygen, how many moles of steam are produced?

    A. 0.5   **B.** 1   **C.** 2   **D.** 3

11. Calcium carbonate can be decomposed by heating.

How many moles of carbon dioxide would be produced by the complete decomposition of 1 mol of calcium carbonate?

   A. 1.0
   B. 0.5
   C. 2.0
   D. It is impossible to say without knowing the temperature and pressure.

12. 1 mol of an alkane required 8 mol of oxygen for complete combustion.

Which of the following is the formula for the alkane?

   A. C_3H_8 **B.** C_4H_{10} **C.** C_5H_{12} **D.** C_6H_{14}

13. Which alkanol will give 7 mol of carbon dioxide when 1 mol of it is completely burned?

   A. $CH_3CH_2CH(OH)CH(CH_3)_2$
   B. $(CH_3)_3CCH_2OH$
   C. $CH_3CH_2CH_2CH(OH)CH_2CH_2CH_3$
   D. $(CH_3)_2CHCH(OH) C(CH_3)_3$

14. If 1 mol of equally fine granules of three metals reacted with equal volumes of excess hydrochloric acid, which one should give off the most hydrogen?

   A. aluminium   **B.** magnesium
   C. lithium   **D.** They should all give same volume.

15. $NO_3^-(aq)$ + $4H^+(aq)$ +   3e $\rightarrow$ $NO(g)$ + $2H_2O(l)$

   $Cu(s)$ $\rightarrow$ $Cu^{2+}(aq)$ +   2e

The equations represent a reaction between nitric acid and copper. How many moles of $NO_3^-(aq)$ are required to oxidise 64 g of copper?

   A. $2/3$ **B.** 1   **C.** $3/2$ **D.** 2

16. A pupil obtained a certain volume of carbon dioxide by the action of $20 \, cm^3$ of hydrochloric acid, concentration 2 mol l^{-1}, on excess of sodium carbonate.

Which reagent gives the same final volume of carbon dioxide when added to excess sodium carbonate?

A. $20 \, cm^3$ of hydrochloric acid, concentration 4 mol l^{-1}

B. $10 \, cm^3$ of hydrochloric acid, concentration 4 mol l^{-1}

C. $20 \, cm^3$ of sulphuric acid, concentration 2 mol l^{-1}

D. $40 \, cm^3$ of hydrochloric acid, concentration 2 mol l^{-1}

In questions 17 to 22 take the molar volume of the gases to be 23.0 litres mol^{-1}.

17. How many litres of oxygen are needed to react completely with 1 mol of calcium?

A. 5.75   **B.** 11.5   **C.** 23.0   **D.** 46.0

18. In the reaction $2C_{(s)} + O_{2(g)} \rightarrow 2CO_{(g)}$
what mass of carbon, in grams, will be used to form 23 litres of CO?

A. 0.6   **B.** 1.2   **C.** 6.0   **D.** 12.0

19. What volume of chlorine, in litres, will be produced when 1 mol of hydrochloric acid reacts according to the equation:

$MnO_{2(s)} + 4HCl_{(aq)} \rightarrow MnCl_{2(aq)} + 2H_2O_{(l)} + Cl_{2(g)}$

A. 5.75   **B.** 11.5   **C.** 23.0   **D.** 92.0

20. How many litres of hydrogen are needed to reduce 1 mol of iron(III) oxide completely to the metal?

A. 11.5   **B.** 23.0   **C.** 46.0   **D.** 69.0

21. Potassium chlorate ($KClO_3$) can decompose on heating to give potassium chloride and oxygen.

What volume of oxygen, in litres, would be produced by the complete decomposition of 1 mol of potassium chlorate?

A. 11.5   **B.** 23.0   **C.** 34.5   **D.** 46

Test 3.7   The idea of excess

Questions 1 to 5 refer to reactions of metals.

For each of the reactions decide whether

A. reactant 1 is in excess   **B.** reactant 2 is in excess
C. neither is in excess.

1. Reactant 1 : 2.4 g of magnesium
   Reactant 2 : 100 cm^3 of hydrochloric acid, concentration 0.2 mol l^{-1}

2. Reactant 1 : 1 g of zinc
   Reactant 2 : 25 cm^3 of copper(II) sulphate solution, concentration 1 mol l^{-1}

3. Reactant 1 : 1.2 g of magnesium
   Reactant 2 : 25 cm^3 of sulphuric acid, concentration 2 mol l^{-1}

4. Reactant 1 : 3.2 g of copper
   Reactant 2 : 100 cm^3 of silver nitrate solution, concentration 1 mol l^{-1}

5. Reactant 1 : 0.6 g of magnesium
   Reactant 2 : 25 cm^3 of hydrochloric acid, concentration 1 mol l^{-1}

6. Hydrochloric acid reacts with magnesium.

   $$Mg(s) \ + \ 2H^+(aq) \ \rightarrow \ Mg^{2+}(aq) \ + \ H_2(g)$$

   What is the minimum volume, in cm^3, of acid, concentration 4 mol l^{-1}, required to react with 0.1 mol of metal?

   A. 25   **B.** 50   **C.** 100   **D.** 200

7. 1.2 g of magnesium is added to 200 cm^3 of hydrochloric acid, concentration 1 mol l^{-1}.

   What is the volume , in litres, of hydrogen produced?

   (Take the molar volume of hydrogen to be 22.8 litres mol^{-1} .)

   A. 0.57   **B.** 1.14   **C.** 2.28   **D.** 4.56

8. 5 g copper powder is added to silver nitrate solution. After some time the powder remaining is filtered off, washed with water and dried.

   The mass of the powder will be

   A. more than 5 g   **B.** equal to 5 g
   C. less than 5 g   **D.** unable to be calculated.

9. Copper carbonate is produced in the reaction of solutions of copper(II) sulphate and sodium carbonate, both of the same concentration.

$$Na_2CO_{3(aq)} + CuSO_{4(aq)} \rightarrow CuCO_{3(s)} + Na_2SO_{4(aq)}$$

Which mixture would give the greatest mass of precipitate?

A. 1.5 cm³ of $Na_2CO_{3(aq)}$ + 0.5 cm³ of $CuSO_{4(aq)}$

B. 0.5 cm³ of $Na_2CO_{3(aq)}$ + 1.5 cm³ of $CuSO_{4(aq)}$

C. 1.0 cm³ of $Na_2CO_{3(aq)}$ + 1.0 cm³ of $CuSO_{4(aq)}$

D. 2.0 cm³ of $Na_2CO_{3(aq)}$ + 0.5 cm³ of $CuSO_{4(aq)}$

10. How much hydrogen would be released by placing 6.5 g of zinc in 205 cm³ of hydrochloric acid, concentration 1 mol l⁻¹?

A. 0.2 mol
B. just over 0.2 mol
C. 0.1 mol
D. just over 0.1 mol

Questions 11 to 14 refer to the addition of 1.2 g of magnesium to 250 cm³ of copper(II) sulphate solution, concentration 1 mol l⁻¹.

Decide whether each of the staements is

A. TRUE   **B.** FALSE.

11. All of the magnesium reacts.

12. 0.025 mol of copper ions react.

13. 3.2 g of copper is displaced.

14. 0.25 mol of magnesium reacts.

Questions 15 to 18 refer to the addition of 64 g of copper to 1 litre of silver nitrate solution, concentration 1 mol l⁻¹.

Decide whether each of the staements is

A. TRUE   **B.** FALSE.

15. The resulting solution is colourless.

16. All the copper dissolves.

17. 64 g of silver is formed.

18. 1 mol of silver is formed.

Test 3.8   Calculations based on equations (ii)

For the questions in this test assume that all measurements are made at the same temperature and pressure.

Questions 1 to 6 refer to reactions involving gases.

Decide whether the total volume of products will be

   A. less than the total volume of reactants
   B. equal to the total volume of reactants
   C. greater than the total volume of reactants.

1. $2NH_{3}(g)$ $\rightarrow$ $N_2(g)$ + $3H_2(g)$

2. $H_2(g)$ + $Cl_2(g)$ $\rightarrow$ $2HCl(g)$

3. $N_2(g)$ + $2O_2(g)$ $\rightarrow$ $2NO_2(g)$

4. $C(s)$ + $O_2(g)$ $\rightarrow$ $CO_2(g)$

5. $C_2H_4(g)$ + $3O_2(g)$ $\rightarrow$ $2CO_2(g)$ + $2H_2O(l)$

6. $CuO(s)$ + $CO(g)$ $\rightarrow$ $Cu(s)$ + $CO_2(g)$

7. The reaction of hydrogen and oxygen is represented by the equation:

   $H_2(g)$ + $^1/_2O_2(g)$ $\rightarrow$ $H_2O(g)$

   What is the volume, in litres, of oxygen which reacts with 1 litre of hydrogen?

   A. $^1/_4$ **B.** $^1/_2$ **C.** 1   **D.** 2

8. $N_2(g)$ + $2O_2(g)$ $\rightarrow$ $2NO_2(g)$

   How many litres of nitrogen dioxide gas could be obtained by sparking 5 litres of nitrogen gas with 2 litres of oxygen gas?

   A. 2   **B.** 3   **C.** 4   **D.** 5

9. What volume of oxygen, in litres, is required for the complete combustion of 1 litre of butane?

   A. 1   **B.** 4   **C.** 6.5   **D.** 13

10. What volume of oxygen, in litres, would be required for the complete combustion of a gaseous mixture containing 1 litre of carbon monoxide and 3 litres of hydrogen?

   A. 1   **B.** 2   **C.** 3   **D.** 4

11. A mixture of 11.2 litres of oxygen and 11.2 litres of hydrogen is sparked.

   What is the total number of molecules which react?
   (Take the molar volume of the gases to be 22.4 litres mol^{-1}.)

   A. 3×10^{23} **B.** 4.5×10^{23}
   C. 6×10^{23} **D.** 9×10^{23}

12. The composition of air by volume is approximately 20% oxygen, 80% nitrogen.

   When air is passed through red-hot carbon, the following reaction occurs:

   $2C(s) + O_2(g) \rightarrow 2CO(g)$

   If all the oxygen is converted to carbon monoxide, what is the composition, by volume, of the gas produced?

   A. 20% carbon monoxide, 80% nitrogen
   B. 33% carbon monoxide, 66% nitrogen
   C. 40% carbon monoxide, 60% nitrogen
   D. 50% carbon monoxide, 50% nitrogen

13. What volume of carbon dioxide, in cm^3, would be obtained by the combustion of 28 cm^3 of carbon monoxide?

   A. 28   **B.** 42   **C.** 56   **D.** 84

14. A volume of 10 cm^3 of carbon monoxide was passed over heated copper(II) oxide until no further reaction occured.

   What volume of gas, in cm^3, was obtained?

   A. 0   **B.** 10   **C.** 15   **D.** 20

15. A mixture of 25 cm^3 of nitrogen and 75 cm^3 of hydrogen is passed over excess heated copper(II) oxide until no further reaction occurs. The products are allowed to cool to room temperature.

   What is the volume, in cm^3, of the remaining gas?

   A. 25   **B.** 50   **C.** 75   **D.** 100

16. A mixture of 60 cm^3 hydrogen and 40 cm^3 of carbon monoxide is passed over excess of heated copper(II) oxide until no further reaction occurs. The products are allowed to cool to room temperature.

What is the volume, in cm^3, of the remaining gas?

   A. 0   **B.** 40   **C.** 60   **D.** 100

Questions 17 and 18 refer to the following experiment.

A mixture of 50 cm^3 of carbon monoxide and 40 cm^3 carbon dioxide is heated with excess copper(II) oxide until no further reaction occurs.

17. What is the total volume of gas, in cm^3, after the reaction?

   A. 40   **B.** 50   **C.** 90   **D.** 140

18. If the gases are **first** passed through an aqueous solution of sodium hydroxide, what is the volume, in cm^3, of the remaining gas?

   A. 40   **B.** 50   **C.** 90   **D.** 140

Questions 19 and 20 refer to the combustion of methane.

15 cm^3 of methane was collected in a tube over mercury and 35 cm^3 of oxygen was added. The mixture was then sparked to burn the methane. The reaction is:

$$CH_4(g) \quad + \quad 2O_2(g) \quad \rightarrow \quad CO_2(g) \quad + \quad 2H_2O(l)$$

19. What was the volume, in cm^3, of the gas remaining after the explosion?

   A. 20   **B.** 45   **C.** 50   **D.** 55

20. If a small volume of sodium hydroxide solution was injected into the tube after the explosion, what would be the volume, in cm^3, of the remaining gas?

   A. 5   **B.** 15   **C.** 30   **D.** 45

Test 3.9

Percentage yields

1. $N_2(g) + 3H_2(g) \rightarrow 2NH_3(g)$

   Under test conditions 10 kg of hydrogen reacts with excess nitrogen to produce 6.5 kg of ammonia.

   Calculate the percentage yield.

   A. 10.0 **B.** 11.5 **C.** 13.0 **D.** 14.5

2. $2SO_2(g) + O_2(g) \rightarrow 2SO_3(g)$

   Under test conditions, 2 kg of sulphur dioxide reacts with excess oxygen to produce 0.5 kg of sulphur trioxide.

   Calculate the percentage yield.

   A. 20 **B.** 25 **C.** 30 **D.** 40

3. $C_2H_4 + H_2O \rightarrow CH_3CH_2OH$
   ethene   ethanol

   Under test conditions, 2.0 kg of ethanol is obtained from 1.5 kg of ethene.

   Calculate the percentage yield.

   A. 75.3 **B.** 77.3 **C.** 79.3 **D.** 81.3

4. propan-2-ol $\rightarrow$ propanone
   $CH_3CH(OH)CH_3$ CH_3COCH_3

   In a preparation, 6.4 g of propanone is obtained from 8.0 g of propan-2-ol.

   Calculate the percentage yield.

   A. 82.8 **B.** 84.0 **C.** 85.2 **D.** 86.4

5. ethanol   +   methanoic acid $\rightarrow$ ethyl methanoate
   CH_3CH_2OH $HCOOH$ $HCOOCH_2CH_3$

   In a preparation, 37 g of ethyl methanoate is obtained from 28.3 g of ethanol.

   Calculate the percentage yield.

   A. 77.3 **B.** 79.3 **C.** 81.3 **D.** 83.3

Test 3.10

Oxidation and reduction

Decide whether each of the reactions involve

A. oxidation　　　　　　　　**B.** reduction.

You may find it helpful to use the data booklet.

1. $Mg^{2+}(aq)$　+　$2e$　→　$Mg(s)$

2. $Ag(s)$　→　$Ag^{+}(aq)$　+　e

3. $2Cl^{-}(aq)$　→　$Cl_2(aq)$　+　$2e$

4. $Fe^{2+}(aq)$　+　$2e$　→　$Fe(s)$

5. $2I^{-}(aq)$　→　$I_2(aq)$

6. $Cu(s)$　→　$Cu^{2+}(aq)$

7. $SO_3^{2-}(aq)$　→　$SO_4^{2-}(aq)$

8. $MnO_4^{-}(aq)$　→　$Mn^{2+}(aq)$

9. iron(II)　→　iron(III)

10. cobalt(III)　→　cobalt(II)

11. zinc atoms　→　zinc ions

12. bromine molecules　→　bromide ions

Test 3.11   Redox reactions

Decide whether each of the following

A. is a redox reaction   **B.** is **NOT** a redox reaction.

1. $Mg(s) + 2H^+(aq) \rightarrow Mg^{2+}(aq) + H_2(g)$

2. $N_2(g) + 3H_2(g) \rightarrow 2NH_3(g)$

3. $H^+(aq) + OH^-(aq) \rightarrow H_2O(l)$

4. $CuO(s) + CO(g) \rightarrow Cu(s) + CO_2(g)$

5. $Br_2(aq) + 2I^-(aq) \rightarrow 2Br^-(aq) + I_2(aq)$

6. $C_2H_4(g) + H_2(g) \rightarrow C_2H_6(g)$

7. $Ba^{2+}(aq) + SO_4^{2-}(aq) \rightarrow BaSO_4(s)$

8. $2Al(s) + 3O_2(g) \rightarrow 2Al_2O_3(s)$

9. $Ca(s) + 2H_2O(l) \rightarrow Ca(OH)_2(aq) + H_2(g)$

10. $Cr_2O_7^{2-}(aq) + 14H^+(aq) + 6I^-(aq) \rightarrow 2Cr^{3+}(aq) + 7H_2O(l) + 3I_2(aq)$

11. $CuO(s) + 2HCl(aq) \rightarrow CuCl_2(aq) + H_2O(l)$

12. $AgNO_3(aq) + NaCl(aq) \rightarrow AgCl(s) + NaNO_3(aq)$

13. $SnCl_2(aq) + HgCl_2(aq) \rightarrow Hg(l) + SnCl_4(aq)$

14. $2Na_2S_2O_3(aq) + I_2(aq) \rightarrow 2NaI(aq) + Na_2S_4O_6(aq)$

15. $2Fe(NO_3)_3(aq) + 2KI(aq) \rightarrow 2Fe(NO_3)_2(aq) + 2KNO_3(aq) + I_2(aq)$

Test 4.1   Fats and oils

In questions 1 to 5 decide whether each of the statements is

A. TRUE   B. FALSE.

1. Fats and oils in the diet supply the body with energy.

2. Carbohydrates are a more concentrated source of energy than fats and oils.

3. Fats are likely to have relatively low melting points compared to oils.

4. Oils have a higher degree of unsaturation than fats.

5. Molecules in fats are packed more closely together than in oils.

6. Fats and oils can be classified as

    A. carbohydrates   B. acids
    C. esters   D. alcohols.

7. The breakdown of fats and oils produces glycerol and

    A. acids   B. alkanes
    C. alkenes   D. esters.

8. What is the structural formula for glycerol?

    A. CH_2OH B. CH_2OH
         $CHOH$ CH_2
         CH_2OH CH_2OH

    C. CH_2OH D. CH_2OH
         CH_2OH $CHOH$
                              CH_2COOH

9. Glycerol can be obtained from a fat by

    A. oxidation
    B. condensation
    C. hydrolysis
    D. esterification.

10. The breakdown of fats and oils produces glycerol and fatty acids in the ratio of

    A. one mole to one mole
    B. one mole to two mole
    C. one mole to three mole
    D. one mole to four mole.

11. What process is represented by the following equation?

$$\begin{array}{l} CH_2-O-\overset{\overset{O}{\parallel}}{C}-C_{17}H_{35} \\[4pt] CH-O-\overset{\overset{O}{\parallel}}{C}-C_{17}H_{35} \quad + \quad 3H_2O \quad \rightarrow \\[4pt] CH_2-O-\overset{\overset{O}{\parallel}}{C}-C_{17}H_{35} \end{array} \qquad \begin{array}{l} CH_2-OH \\[4pt] CH-OH \quad + \quad 3C_{17}H_{35}COOH \\[4pt] CH_2-OH \end{array}$$

    A. condensation   **B.** hydrolysis
    C. oxidation   **D.** dehydration

12. The conversion of linoleic acid, $C_{18}H_{32}O_2$, into stearic acid, $C_{18}H_{36}O_2$, is likely to be achieved by

    A. hydrogenation   **B.** hydrolysis
    C. hydration   **D.** dehydrogenation.

13. A vegetable oil is mixed with hydrogen under pressure at about 200 °C in the presence of a catalyst.

The hydrogen

    A. dissolves in the oil without reacting
    B. combines with oxygen in the oil
    C. makes the unsaturated oil saturated
    D. makes the oil polymerise.

Questions 14 and 15 refer to kinds of reaction.

    A. hydrolysis   **B.** dehydration
    C. hydrogenation   **D.** condensation

14. What reaction can be used to describe the breakdown of fats during digestion?

15. What reaction can be used to describe the process by which some liquid oils can be converted into solid fats?

Test 4.2   Simple esters - structures and names

In question 1 to 20 decide whether each of the organic compounds

A. is an ester   **B.** is **NOT** an ester.

1. methanol

2. ethyl methanoate

3. hexanone

4. butanoic acid

5. methyl propanoate

6. pentanal

7.

$$CH_3-\overset{\displaystyle O}{\overset{\|}{C}}-O-CH_2\,CH_3$$

8. CH_3CH_2OH

9. CH_3-O-CH_3

10.

$$CH_3-\overset{\displaystyle O}{\overset{\|}{C}}-OH$$

11. $CH_3-\overset{\displaystyle O}{\overset{\|}{C}}-CH_3$

12.

$$CH_3-O-\overset{\displaystyle O}{\overset{\|}{C}}-CH_3$$

13.

$$CH_3-\overset{\displaystyle O}{\overset{\|}{C}}-O-CH_3$$

14.

$$CH_3-\overset{\displaystyle O}{\overset{\|}{C}}-H$$

15. $CH_3CH_2COOCH_3$

16. CH_3CH_2COOH

17. $CH_3CH_2CH_2OH$

18. CH_3CH_2CHO

19. CH_3OCOCH_3

20. $CH_3CH_2COCH_2CH_3$

Questions 21 to 24 refer to names of esters.

21. What ester is formed in the reaction of methanol with ethanoic acid?

   A. methyl ethanoate   **B.** ethyl methanoate

22. What ester is formed in the reaction of propanol with methanoic acid?

   A. methyl propanoate   **B.** propyl methanoate

23. What ester is formed in the reaction of ethanoic acid with butanol?

   A. butyl ethanoate   **B.** ethyl butanoate

24. What ester is formed in the reaction of butanoic acid with methanol?

   A. butyl methanoate   **B.** methyl butanoate

Questions 25 to 28 refer to structures of esters.

A.

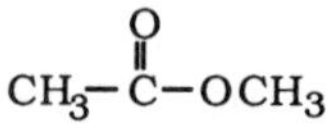

$$CH_3-\overset{\overset{\displaystyle O}{\|}}{C}-OCH_3$$

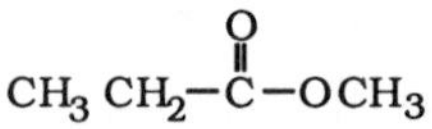

B.

$$CH_3\ CH_2-\overset{\overset{\displaystyle O}{\|}}{C}-OCH_3$$

C.

$$CH_3\ CH_2\ O-\overset{\overset{\displaystyle O}{\|}}{C}-CH_3$$

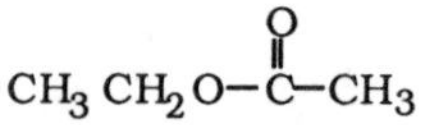

D.

$$CH_3\ CH_2\ O-\overset{\overset{\displaystyle O}{\|}}{C}-H$$

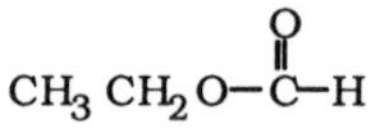

25. What is the structure of the ester formed in the reaction between ethanol and methanoic acid?

26. What is the structure of the ester formed in the reaction between propanoic acid and methanol?

27. What is the structure of ethyl ethanoate?

28. What is the structure of methyl ethanoate?

Test 4.3   Simple esters - properties and reactions

In questions 1 to 6 decide whether each of the statements about
methyl ethanoate is

  A. TRUE   **B.** FALSE.

1. It is soluble in water.
2. It has a characteristic smell.
3. It is a conductor of electricity.

4. It is flammable.
5. It is made up of molecules.
6. It turns Universal indicator solution red.

Questions 7 and 8 refer to the reaction of ethanoic acid and an alcohol in
the presence of concentrated sulphuric acid.

7. The product is

  A. a hydrocarbon   **B.** an ester
  C. a salt   **D.** a carbohydrate.

8. The reaction can be considered to be an example of

  A. precipitation   **B.** distillation
  C. condensation   **D.** neutralisation.

9. The formation of ethanol from ethyl ethanoate is an example of

  A. condensation   **B.** dehydration
  C. hydration   **D.** hydrolysis.

10. Two flasks, **X** and **Y**,
with their contents as
shown,were placed in
a vessel of water at 40 ^{0} C.

water at 40 ^{o}C

methanol + ethanoic acid   methyl ethanoate + water
+ concentrated sulphuric acid + concentrated sulphuric acid

After several hours the contents of both flasks were analysed.

Which of the following would be expected?

  A. Flask **X** contains methyl ethanoate, methanol and ethanoic acid; flask **Y** is unchanged.
  B. Flask **X** and flask **Y** both contain methyl ethanoate, methanol and ethanoic acid.
  C. Flask **X** contains methyl ethanoate; flask **Y** is unchanged.
  D. Flask **X** contains methyl ethanoate; flask **Y** contains methyl ethanoate, methanol and ethanoic acid.

Test 4.4   Proteins

1. Proteins are substances which, in addition to carbon, hydrogen and oxygen, always contain

   A. phosphorus   **B.** nitrogen
   C. sulphur   **D.** calcium.

2.

   $$H-\overset{\overset{\displaystyle CH_3}{|}}{\underset{\underset{\displaystyle CH_3}{|}}{C}}-\overset{\overset{\displaystyle NH_2}{|}}{\underset{\underset{\displaystyle H}{|}}{C}}-C\overset{\displaystyle O}{\underset{\displaystyle OH}{}}$$

   The molecule can be classified as

   A. an amino acid   **B.** an ester
   C. a peptide   **D.** a protein.

   Questions 3 and 4 refer to the breakdown of protein during digestion to give smaller molecules.

3. Which compound might be obtained by the breakdown of protein?

   A. glucose   **B.** glycerol
   C. stearic acid   **D.** amino-ethanoic acid

4. What name can be given to the process which takes place?

   A. dehydration   **B.** condensation
   C. hydrogenation   **D.** hydrolysis

5. Essential amino acids are defined as the amino acids which

   A. are necessary for building polypeptides
   B. humans must acquire through their diets
   C. plants cannot synthesise for themselves
   D. are produced in the breakdown of any protein.

6. In which kind of compound is nitrogen always present?

   A. enzymes   **B.** oils
   C. polyesters   **D.** carbohydrates

7. Which of the following could represent part of a protein structure?

A.
$$-\overset{\displaystyle H}{\underset{\displaystyle H}{C}}-O-\overset{\displaystyle H}{N}-\overset{\displaystyle H}{\underset{\displaystyle H}{C}}-O-$$

B.
$$-\overset{\displaystyle O}{C}-\overset{\displaystyle H}{N}-\overset{\displaystyle H}{\underset{\displaystyle H}{C}}-\overset{\displaystyle O}{C}-\overset{\displaystyle H}{N}-$$

C.
$$-\overset{\displaystyle OH}{C}=N-\overset{\displaystyle H}{\underset{\displaystyle H}{C}}-\overset{\displaystyle OH}{C}=N-$$

D.
$$-\overset{\displaystyle H}{\underset{\displaystyle H}{C}}-\overset{\displaystyle O}{C}-O-\overset{\displaystyle H}{N}-\overset{\displaystyle H}{\underset{\displaystyle H}{C}}-$$

8. What type of chemical reaction takes place in the formation of proteins from amino acids?

    A. condensation
    B. hydration
    C. hydrolysis
    D. dehydration

9. Which nitrogen containing compound could be a starting material for protein synthesis?

    A. $Pb(NO_3)_2$
    B. $(NH_4)_2SO_4$
    C. $H_2N(CH_2)_4NH_2$
    D. $(CH_3)_2C(NH_2)COOH$

10. When two amino acids join together a peptide link is formed.

    Which of the following represents this process?

A.

B.

C.

D.

11. On complete breakdown, a peptide produced 5 amino acids represented by the letters **P, Q, R, S** and **T**. The following fragments were produced on partial breakdown.

Peptide $\xrightarrow{\text{partial breakdown}}$ **TS + QP + RT + SQ**

Which sequence could be the correct one for the arrangement of amino acids in the peptide?

A. **P-T-S-Q-R**
B. **R-T-S-P-Q**
C. **Q-P-T-S-R**
D. **R-T-S-Q-P**

12. Which of the following is the most likely optimum temperature for human enzyme activity?

A. close to 20 ^{o}C
B. close to 40 ^{o}C
C. close to 60 ^{o}C
D. close to 80 ^{o}C

Test 5.1   Bonding in the first twenty elements

The questions in this test refer to types of structure.

    A. metallic
    B. covalent (network)
    C. covalent (discrete molecular gas)
    D. covalent (discrete molecular solid)
    E. monatomic

What is the type of structure which predominates at room temperature in each of the elements?

1.	aluminium	11.	hydrogen
2.	argon	12.	lithium
3.	beryllium	13.	neon
4.	nitrogen	14.	boron
5.	calcium	15.	oxygen
6.	carbon	16.	phosphorus
7.	sulphur	17.	potassium
8.	fluorine	18.	silicon
9.	magnesium	19.	sodium
10.	helium	20.	chlorine

Test 5.2   Bonding in elements and compounds

Questions 1 to 5 refer to types of structure.

A. covalent (discrete molecules)   **B.** covalent (network)
C. ionic

What type of structure predominates in each of the compounds?

1. hydrogen oxide   4. magnesium oxide

2. sodium oxide   5. silicon oxide

3. sulphur dioxide

Questions 6 to 13 refer to intermolecular attractions.

A. van der Waals' forces   **B.** hydrogen bonds

What is the main intermolecular attraction in each of the liquids?

6. neon   10. hydrogen oxide

7. butane   11. nitrogen hydride

8. hydrogen fluoride   12. methanol

9. hydrogen   13. octene

Question 14 to 21 refer to types of attraction.

A. non-polar covalent bonds   **B.** polar covalent bonds
C. hydrogen bonds   **D.** van der Waals' forces

What type of attraction is mainly responsible for holding each of the pairs together?

14. two adjacent ethanol molecules

15. the carbon atom and a chlorine atom in a molecule of tetrachloromethene

16. two chlorine atoms in a molecule of chlorine

17. two adjacent argon atoms in solid argon

18. a hydrogen atom and the oxygen atom in a molecule of water

19. two adjacent hexene molecules in hexene

20. the carbon atom and an oxygen atom in a molecule of carbon dioxide

21. two adjacent molecules of hydrogen fluoride

Questions 22 to 25 refer to types of structure.

A. three dimensional ionic lattice
B. three dimensional covalently linked structure
C. three dimensional structure of molecules, linked by hydrogen bonds
D. linear covalent structure, linked by van der Waals' forces

Which type best describes the structure of each of the following?

22. ice

23. silicon dioxide

24. potassium chloride

25. polystyrene

Questions 26 to 29 refer to types of attraction.

A. covalent bonds   **B.** hydrogen bonds
C. ionic bonds   **D.** van der Waal's forces

What type of attraction is overcome in melting each of the following?

26. caesium fluoride

27. hydrogen fluoride

28. fluorine

29. silicon

Question 30 and 31 refer to types of bonding.

A. metallic
B. polar covalent
C. non-polar covalent
D. ionic

Which type of bonding is likely to be present in each of the following?

30. an element which melts at 3500 °C and forms a gaseous oxide

31. a compound which boils at 185 K

Questions 32 to 35 refer to types of attraction.

Decide whether each of the following is

A. intermolecular	**B.** **NOT** intermolecular.

32. covalent bonds

33. ionic bonds

34. hydrogen bonds

35. metallic bonds

36. van der Waals' forces

Questions 37 to 39 refer to the formation of chlorides.

A. lithium	**B.** caesium
C. sulphur	**D.** phosphorus
E. xenon	

37. Which element forms the chloride which is most ionic in character?

38. Which element forms the chloride which is most covalent in character?

39. Which element is least likely to form a chloride?

40. Which pair of elements would be expected to react together with the greatest release of energy?

    A. potassium and bromine
    B. caesium and fluorine
    C. lithium and iodine
    D. sodium and chlorine

41. In general, covalent substances have lower melting points than ionic substances because

    A. ionic bonds are stronger than covalent bonds
    B. covalent compounds are composed of non-metals which have low melting points
    C. bonds between molecules are weaker than bonds between ions
    D. covalent bonds have no electrostatic forces.

42. Information about four solids, **A**, **B**, **C** and **D**, is shown.

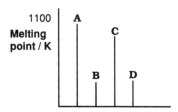

Electrical conduction of solid	
A.	non-conductor
B.	conductor
C.	conductor
D.	non-conductor

In which solid is it most likely that only van der Waals' forces are overcome when the substance melts?

43.

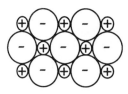

Substance **X**, molecular mass 62	Substance **Y**, molecular mass 64.5

From a consideration of chemical bonding, what can you predict about the boiling points of these compounds?

A. The boiling point of **X** is greater than that of **Y**.
B. The boiling point of **X** is less than that of **Y**.
C. The boiling point of **X** is approximately equal to that of **Y**.
D. Nothing can be predicted.

44. In the diagram, each sphere represents a particle about the size of an atom and the sign indicates the charge on the particle.

For which substance would the model be a reasonable representation of the particles and the way they are arranged in the crystal?

A. tetrabromomethane
B. calcium flouride
C. lithium bromide
D. diamond

Questions 45 and 46 refer to the diagrams which represent molecules.

(i)

(ii)

| represents an electron pair in the plane of the paper;

△ represents an electron pair in front of the plane of the paper;

⋱ represents an electron pair behind the plane of the paper.

45. Which elements could make up structure (i) ?

	R	T
A.	nitrogen	hydrogen
B.	hydrogen	nitrogen
C.	carbon	hydrogen
D.	beryllium	chlorine

46. Which elements could make up structure (ii) ?

	Z	Q
A.	oxygen	hydrogen
B.	hydrogen	oxygen
C.	beryllium	hydrogen
D.	phosphorus	hydrogen

47. The diagram shows the melting points of successive elements across a period in the Periodic Table.

Melting point / K

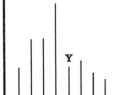

Which is a correct reason for the low melting point of element **Y**?

A. It has weak ionic bonds.

B. It has weak covalent bonds.

C. It has weakly held outer electrons.

D. It has weak forces between molecules.

Test 5.3

Properties of elements and compounds

In questions 1 to 9 decide whether each of the substances

A. conducts electricity   **B.** does **NOT** conduct electricity.

1. liquid oxygen

2. solid phosphorus pentachloride

3. molten potassium chloride

4. liquid tetrachloromethane

5. solid sodium chloride

6. molten copper

7. solid sulphur

8. calcium chloride solution

9. solid iron

Questions 10 to 15 refer to types of bonding.

A. covalent (discrete molecules)   **B.** ionic
C. covalent (network structure)   **D.** metallic

Which type of bonding predominates in each of the following?

10. a substance which melts at 1044 °C and which conducts electricity when molten, but not when solid

11. a substance which melts at 962 °C and conducts electricity when solid

12. a substance which melts at 843 °C and boils at 1540 °C; when an electric current is passed through the molten substance no decomposition occurs

13. a substance of melting point 2300 °C, boiling point of 2550 °C, which does not conduct electricity

14. a substance melting at 1074 °C and boiling at 1740 °C: the passage of an electric current through the molten substance results in decomposition

15. a substance which melts at 6 °C and boils at 80 °C, which does not conduct electricity

Questions 16 to 19 refer to properties of elements and compounds.

A.	potassium fluoride	**B.**	silicon oxide
C.	sulphur	**D.**	sodium

16. Which is a solid of low melting point with high electrical conductivity?

17. Which is a non-conducting solid which becomes a good conductor on melting?

18. Which is a solid of high melting point with no electrical conductivity?

19. Which is a solid of low melting point with no electrical conductivity?

20. Which substance is insoluble in water but soluble in tetrachloromethane?

A.	iodine	**B.**	sodium chloride
C.	potassium iodide	**D.**	lithium bromide

21. Which statement is correct?

An ionic compound is likely to

    A. have a low melting point
    B. dissolve in non-polar solvents
    C. be an electrical insulator when molten
    D. be soluble in water.

22. Silicon carbide can be used as

    A. a lubricant
    B. a tip for cutting / grinding tools
    C. a substitute for pencil 'lead'
    D. an electrical conductor.

In questions 23 to 28 decide whether each of the covalent compounds

    A. reacts with water forming ions
    B. does **NOT** react with water forming ions.

23.	HBr	26.	C_2H_6
24.	CCl_4	27.	NH_3
25.	SO_2	28.	C_3H_6

Test 5.4   Polarity of molecules

Decide whether each of the molecules is

A.   overall polar   **B.**   overall non-polar.

1. H_2

2. CH_4

3. HCl

4. H_2O

5. CO_2

6. NH_3

7. $CHCl_3$

8. CH_3OH

Test 5.5   Displacement reactions

In question 1 to 6 decide whether

A. a reaction will take place   **B.** a reaction will **NOT** take place.

1. chlorine gas bubbled through sodium bromide solution

2. bromine water bubbled through potassium iodide solution

3. iodine solution added to sodium chloride solution

4. chlorine water added to potassium fluoride solution

5. fluorine gas bubbled through sodium iodide solution

6. bromine water added to potassium chloride solution

Questions 7 and 8 refer to the reaction which takes place when bromine is added to a solution of sodium iodide containing starch.

7. What is observed in this reaction?

   A. A deep blue colour forms.
   B. A yellow precipitate forms.
   C. A white precipitate forms.
   D. An orange colour forms.

8. What is the best explanation for the observation?

   A. The iodide ion has a smaller radius than the iodine atom.
   B. The iodide ion has a stronger hold on its outer electrons than does the bromide ion.
   C. The element with the greater number of electrons will always give electrons to an element with fewer electrons per atom.
   D. Bromine atoms have a greater attraction for electrons than iodine atoms.

Test 5.6

Trends in the elements

Questions 1 to 9 refer to trends associated with increasing atomic number in the alkali metals.

Decide whether each of the statements is

A. TRUE   **B.** FALSE.

1. The metallic bond strength increases.

2. The ionisation energy decreases.

3. The covalent radius decreases.

4. The number of occupied energy levels decreases.

5. The attraction for bonded electrons decreases.

6. The melting point increases.

7. The tendancy to form positive ions increases.

8. The nuclear charge increases.

9. The relative atomic mass decreases.

Questions 10 to 18 refer to trends associated with increasing atomic number in the halogens.

Decide whether each of the statements is

A. TRUE   **B.** FALSE.

10. The tendency to form negative ions decreases.

11. The density decreases.

12. The first ionisation energy increases.

13. The boiling point increases.

14. The nuclear charge increases.

15. The attraction for bonded electrons increases.

16. The relative atomic mass increases.

17. The covalent radius increases.

18. The number of occupied energy levels increases.

Questions 19 to 23 refer to trends associated with increasing atomic number in the elements in the second period of the Periodic Table.

Decide whether each of the statements is

A. TRUE　　　　　　　　　**B.** FALSE.

19. The ionisation energy increases.

20. The number of occupied energy levels increases.

21. The nuclear charge decreases.

22. The covalent radius increases.

23. The attraction for bonded electrons decreases.

Questions 24 and 25 refer to properties of elements.

A. caesium　　　　　　　　**B.** oxygen
C. fluorine　　　　　　　　**D.** iodine

24. Which element has the greatest attraction for bonded electrons?

25. Which element has the lowest ionisation energy?

26. Which property of the Group 1 elements could be represented by the graph?

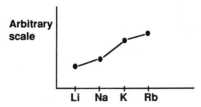

A. the first ionisation energy　　**B.** the melting point
C. the atomic radius　　　　　　**D.** the attraction for bonded electrons

27. Potassium has a larger covalent radius than sodium because potassium has

A. a larger nuclear charge
B. a larger nucleus
C. more occupied energy levels
D. a larger ionisation energy.

28. Which statement concerning the radii of atoms and ions is correct?

The radius of

A. Cl^- is less than that of Cl
B. H^- is greater than that of H^+
C. Na^+ is greater than that of Na
D. Fe^{3+} is greater than that of Fe^{2+}.

Questions 29 to 33 refer to the element francium.

Decide whether each of the statements is likely to be

A. TRUE   **B.** FALSE.

29. It will resist corrosion.

30. It will form a covalent chloride.

31. It will form a soluble hydroxide.

32. It will be very reactive.

33. It will conduct electricity.

Questions 34 to 38 refer to the element astatine.

Decide whether each of the statements is likely to be

A. TRUE   **B.** FALSE.

34. It will exist as diatomic molecules.

35. It will be a gas at room temperature.

36. It will form an ionic compound with sodium.

37. It will conduct electricity.

38. It will form a covalent hydride.

Test 5.7   Oxides, chlorides and hydrides

1. Which of the oxides will have the highest melting point?

    A. barium oxide   **B.** sulphur trioxide
    C. carbon dioxide   **D.** selenium oxide

2. Which of the oxides is a high melting point solid?

    A. carbon oxide   **B.** sulphur dioxide
    C. silicon dioxide   **D.** nitrogen dioxide

3. Which oxide would be a solid at room temperature (298 K) and a gas at 500 K?

    A. fluorine oxide   **B.** phosphorus oxide
    C. magnesium oxide   **D.** boron oxide

Questions 4 to 7 refer to properties of oxides.

    A. aluminium oxide   **B.** carbon dioxide
    C. sodium oxide   **D.** hydrogen oxide

4. Which oxide is least acidic?

5. Which oxide is most acidic?

6. Which is an amphoteric oxide?

7. Which is a neutral oxide?

8. Which element is least likely to form a chloride?

    A. B   **B.** Si   **C.** Cs   **D.** Xe

9. Which chloride will have the highest melting point?

    A. strontium chloride   **B.** nitrogen chloride
    C. silicon chloride   **D.** sulphur chloride

10. Which chloride reacts with water to produce fumes of hydrogen chloride?

    A. magnesium chloride   **B.** sodium chloride
    C. silicon chloride   **D.** strontium chloride

11. Which chloride is most likely to be soluble in tetrachlormethane, CCl_4?

    A. barium chloride   **B.** caesium chloride

    C. calcium chloride   **D.** phosphorus chloride

12. Which chloride is most likely to be present in a sample of strontium chloride?

    A. barium chloride   **B.** aluminium chloride

    C. rubidium chloride   **D.** cadmium chloride

13. During electrolysis of a molten substance, hydrogen is evolved at the positive electrode.

The substance could be

    A. selenium hydride   **B.** silicon hydride

    C. nitrogen hydride   **D.** lithium hydride.

Questions 14 and 15 refer to hydrides of elements.

    A. sodium   **B.** nitrogen

    C. silicon   **D.** chlorine

14. Which hydride, when added to water, would give the most acidic solution?

15. Which hydride will have the highest melting point?

16. Which statement is correct?

    A. Lithium hydride is ionic.

    B. Rubidium hydride is covalent.

    C. Alkali metal hydrides are made by reducing the metal with hydrogen.

    D. Alkali metal hydrides are made by reducing the metal oxide with hydrogen.

17. Which compound contains hydride ions?

    A. HCl

    B. H_2O

    C. NH_3

    D. NaH

Test 6.1   Heat of neutralisation

The questions in this test refer to rises in temperature.

A. 2.5 °C   **B.**   5 °C   **C.**   10 °C

When 50 cm³ of HCl(aq), concentration 1 mol l⁻¹, reacts with 50 cm³ of NaOH(aq), concentration 1 mol l⁻¹, the approximate temperature rise is 5 °C.

What will be the approximate temperature rise in each of the reactions?

1. 50 cm³ HNO_3(aq), (1 mol l⁻¹)   50 cm³ NaOH(aq), (1 mol l⁻¹)

2. 50 cm³ HCl(aq), (1 mol l⁻¹)   50 cm³ KOH(aq), (1 mol l⁻¹)

3. 100 cm³ HCl(aq), (1 mol l⁻¹)   100 cm³ NaOH(aq), (1 mol l⁻¹)

4. 25 cm³ HCl(aq), (1 mol l⁻¹)   25 cm³ NaOH(aq), (1 mol l⁻¹)

5. 100 cm³ HCl(aq), (0.5 mol l⁻¹)   100 cm³ NaOH(aq), (0.5 mol l⁻¹)

6. 100 cm³ HCl(aq), (2 mol l⁻¹)   100 cm³ NaOH(aq), (2 mol l⁻¹)

7. 50 cm³ HCl(aq), (2 mol l⁻¹)   50 cm³ NaOH(aq), (2 mol l⁻¹)

8. 100 cm³ HCl(aq), (2 mol l⁻¹)   100 cm³ NaOH(aq), (1 mol l⁻¹)

9. 50 cm³ H_2SO_4(aq), (1 mol l⁻¹)   50 cm³ NaOH(aq), (1 mol l⁻¹)

10. 25 cm³ H_2SO_4(aq), (1 mol l⁻¹)   25 cm³ NaOH(aq), (2 mol l⁻¹)

11. 25 cm³ HCl (aq), (0.5 mol l⁻¹)   25 cm³ NaOH(aq), (1 mol l⁻¹)

12. 25 cm³ H_2SO_4(aq), (0.5 mol l⁻¹)   25cm³ NaOH(aq), (1 mol l⁻¹)

Test 6.2

Enthalpy changes (i)

1. When 1 g of an alcohol (formula mass 46) is burned 30 kJ of energy is released.

   What is the enthalpy of combustion, in kJ mol^{-1}, of the alcohol?

   A. -30   **B.** -1380
   C. -650   **D.** -1920

2. What is the enthalpy change, in kJ, when 3.2 g of methanol is burned?

   (Use the enthalpy of combustion information in the data booklet.)

   A. -71.5   **B.** +71.5   **C.** -715   **D.** +715

3. $H^+(aq)$ + $OH^-(aq)$ $\rightarrow$ $H_2O(l)$ $\Delta H = -57.5$ kJ mol^{-1}

   What is the amount of heat produced, in kJ, when 4.00 g of NaOH is just neutralised by $HCl(aq)$?

   A. 5.75   **B.** 28.7   **C.** 7.5   **D.** 15

4. What is the mass of ethanol, in grams, which has to be burned to produce 13.71 kJ?

   (Use the enthalpy of combustion information in the data booklet.)

   A. 0.46   **B.** 4.6   **C.** 13.71   **D.** 1371

5. When 1 g of a compound (formula mass 56) is dissolved in 50 cm^3 of water, the temperature rises by 4.7 ^oC.

   What is the enthalpy of solution of the compound?

   A. -55.0 J mol^{-1} **B.** -5.50 kJ mol^{-1}
   C. -5.50 J mol^{-1} **D.** -55.0 kJ mol^{-1}

6. When 2.24 litres of a gas was burned, the heat produced warmed 2 litres of water from 12 ^oC to 38 ^oC.

   What is the enthalpy of combustion, in kJ mol^{-1}, of the gas?
   (Take the molar volume to be 22.4 l mol^{-1}.)

   A. -2084   **B.** -2284
   C. -2174   **D.** -2374

Question 1 to 12 refer to enthalpy (energy) changes.

A.	formation	**B.**	combustion
C.	sublimation	**D.**	solution
E.	ionisation	**F.**	hydration
G.	lattice	**H.**	electron gain

What change would refer to each of the reactions?
(Note that there are **two** correct answers to question 3.)

1. $C(s) \rightarrow C(g)$

2. $Cl(g) + e \rightarrow Cl^-(g)$

3. $2H_2(g) + O_2(g) \rightarrow 2H_2O(l)$

4. $Mg^{2+}(g) + (aq) \rightarrow Mg^{2+}(aq)$

5. $CH_4(g) + 2O_2(g) \rightarrow CO_2(g) + 2H_2O(g)$

6. $Mg(g) \rightarrow Mg^{2+}(g) + 2e$

7. $NaCl(s) \rightarrow Na^+(g) + Cl^-(g)$

8. $KOH(s) + (aq) \rightarrow K^+(aq) + OH^-(aq)$

9. $C(s) + H_2(g) + Cl_2(g) \rightarrow CH_2Cl_2(g)$

10. $Mg^{2+}(g) + O^{2-}(g) \rightarrow MgO(s)$

11. $I_2(g) \rightarrow I_2(s)$

12. $Br^-(g) + (aq) \rightarrow Br^-(aq)$

Questions 13 to 20 refer to energy changes during reactions.

A. endothermic   **B.** exothermic

C. either endothermic or exothermic

Which kind of energy change takes place during each of the reactions?

13. combustion   17. electron gain

14. formation   18. hydration

15. ionisation   19. lattice breaking

16. solution   20. bond dissociation

Test 6.4   Enthalpy changes (iii)

In questions 1 to 4 decide whether each of the following

A. can be measured directly by experiment
B. can **NOT** be measured directly by experiment.

1. the enthalpy of combustion of methanol

2. the bond energy of the C-H bond in $CH_{4(g)}$

3. the enthalpy of solution of sodium hydroxide

4. the enthalpy of formation of ethane

5. Which process represents the enthalpy of formation of ethanol?

A. $2C_{(s)} + 2H_{2(g)} + H_2O_{(g)} \rightarrow C_2H_5OH_{(l)}$

B. $2C_{(s)} + 6H_{(g)} + O_{(g)} \rightarrow C_2H_5OH_{(g)}$

C. $2C_{(g)} + 3H_{2(g)} + {}^1/_2O_{2(g)} \rightarrow C_2H_5OH_{(g)}$

D. $2C_{(s)} + 3H_{2(g)} + {}^1/_2O_{2(g)} \rightarrow C_2H_5OH_{(l)}$

6. The bond enthalpy of the C-H bond is equal to one quarter of the value of ΔH for one of the following reactions.

Which one?

A. $C_{(g)} + 2H_{2(g)} \rightarrow CH_{4(g)}$

B. $CH_{4(g)} \rightarrow C_{(s)} + 4H_{(g)}$

C. $CH_{4(g)} \rightarrow C_{(g)} + 4H_{(g)}$

D. $CH_{4(g)} \rightarrow C_{(g)} + 2H_{2(g)}$

7. The mean bond enthalpy of the C-H bond is 416 kJ mol^{-1}.

It can be calculated that 1656 kJ of energy

A. is evolved when one mole of methane is burned in excess oxygen

B. is required to dissociate one mole of methane into free carbon and hydrogen atoms

C. is evolved when one mole of graphite combines with two moles of hydrogen gas

D. is required for the complete combustion of one mole of methane.

8. Which process represents the enthalpy of combustion of ethane?

   A.. $C_2H_6(g)$ + $7O(g)$ → $2CO_2(g)$ + $3H_2O(l)$

   B. $C_2H_6(g)$ → $2C(g)$ + $6H(g)$

   C. $C_2H_6(g)$ + $3^1/_2O_2(g)$ → $2CO_2(g)$ + $3H_2O(l)$

   D. $2C(g)$ + $3H_2(g)$ → $C_2H_6(g)$

9. The enthalpy of formation of tetrachloromethane (CCl_4) is -139 kJ mol^{-1}.

   From this information it can be concluded that

   A. 139 kJ is evolved when one mole of CCl_4 is burned in oxygen

   B. when one mole of graphite combines with two moles of chlorine gas 139 kJ is evolved

   C. 139 kJ is required to dissociate one mole of CCl_4 into free carbon and chlorine atoms

   D. 139 kJ is evolved when one mole of graphite combines with four moles of chlorine atoms.

10. Consider the table of mean bond enthalpies.

Bond	Mean bond enthalpy / kJ mol^{-1}
C - C	348
C - H	415
Si - Si	176
Si - H	318

Which statement can be considered to be consistent with the values?

   A. 348 kJ is the energy evolved when one mole of graphite sublimes.
   B. Methane, CH_4, is chemically more stable than silane, SiH_4.
   C. Si-Si bonds are the least readily broken of those listed.
   D. Si-Si chains are more stable than C-C chains.

11. Which process can be described as an enthalpy of formation?

   A. $C_2H_4(g)$ + $H_2(g)$ → $C_2H_6(g)$

   B. $2C(s)$ + $3H_2(g)$ → $C_2H_6(g)$

   C. $2C(g)$ + $6H(g)$ → $C_2H_6(g)$

   D. $C_2H_2(g)$ + $2H_2(g)$ → $C_2H_6(g)$

12. The mean bond enthalpy of the N-H bond is equal to one third of the value of ΔH for which change?

    A. $N_{(g)} \;+\; 3H_{(g)} \;\rightarrow\; NH_{3(g)}$

    B. $N_{2(g)} \;+\; 3H_{2(g)} \;\rightarrow\; 2NH_{3(g)}$

    C. $^1/_2N_{2(g)} \;+\; 1^1/_2H_{2(g)} \;\rightarrow\; NH_{3(g)}$

    D. $2NH_{3(g)} \;+\; 1^1/_2O_{2(g)} \;\rightarrow\; N_{2(g)} \;+\; 3H_2O_{(g)}$

13. The enthalpy of solution of an ionic salt is numerically equal to the difference between the enthalpies of

    A. hydration and lattice-breaking

    B. neutralisation and hydration

    C. lattice-breaking and elecrtron gain

    D. electron gain and neutralisation.

Test 6.5

1. $C_{(s)}$ + $O_{2(g)}$ → $CO_{2(g)}$ $\Delta H = -395$ kJ mol^{-1}

   $CO_{(g)}$ + $^1/_2 O_{2(g)}$ → $CO_{2(g)}$ $\Delta H = -282$ kJ mol^{-1}

   What is the enthalpy of formation, in kJ mol^{-1}, of carbon monoxide?

   A. +113   **B.** -677   **C.** -113   **D.** -197.5

2. Given the equations:

   $Mg_{(s)}$ + $2H^+_{(aq)}$ → $Mg^{2+}_{(aq)}$ + $H_{2(g)}$ $\Delta H = $ **a** J mol^{-1}

   $Zn_{(s)}$ + $2H^+_{(aq)}$ → $Zn^{2+}_{(aq)}$ + $H_{2(g)}$ $\Delta H = $ **b** J mol^{-1}

   $Mg_{(s)}$ + $Zn^{2+}_{(aq)}$ → $Mg^{2+}_{(aq)}$ + $Zn_{(s)}$ $\Delta H = $ **c** J mol^{-1}

   then according to Hess's Law

   A. **a - b = c**   **B.** **a + b = c**
   C. **a + c = b**   **D.** **a - b = c.**

3. C_2H_2 + $2H_2$ → C_2H_6

   What is the enthalpy, in kJ mol^{-1}, for the complete hydrogenation of one mole of ethyne, C_2H_2 ?

   (Use the information in the data booklet on enthalpies of combustion.)

   A. -49   **B.** -335   **C.** -237   **D.** -3419

4. The reaction for the complete combustion of dichloromethane may be represented:

   CH_2Cl_2 + O_2 → CO_2 + 2HCl $\Delta H = -446$ kJ mol^{-1}

   Assuming that the enthalpies of formation of carbon dioxide and hydrogen chloride are -395 kJ mol^{-1} and -92 kJ mol^{-1} respectively, what is the enthalpy of formation, in kJ mol^{-1}, of dichloromethane?

   A. -133   **B.** -41   **C.** +143   **D.** +749

5. Given that the enthalpies of formation of iron(III) oxide and aluminium oxide are -827 kJ mol^{-1} and -1676 kJ mol^{-1} respectively, the enthalpy change, in kJ mol^{-1}, for the reaction Fe_2O_3 + $2Al$ → $2Fe$ + Al_2O_3 is given by

   A. -827 + 1676   **B.** 2(-827 + 1676)
   C. +827-1676   **D.** $^1/_2$ (827 - 1676).

6. Given that the enthalpies of combustion of carbon, hydrogen and ethane are **X**, **Y** and **Z** kJ mol^{-1} respectively, what is the enthalpy of formation, in kJ mol^{-1}, of ethane?

A. (2**X** + 3**Y** - **Z**)
B. (2**X** + 3**Y** + **Z**)
C. (**X** + **Y** - **Z**)
D. (-2**X** - 3**Y** + **Z**)

7. $N_2(g)$ + $2O_2(g)$ → $2NO_2(g)$ ΔH = +88 kJ mol^{-1}
   $N_2(g)$ + $2O_2(g)$ → $N_2O_4(g)$ ΔH = +10 kJ mol^{-1}

The enthalpy change, in kJ mol^{-1}, for the reaction $2NO_2(g)$ → $N_2O_4(g)$ will be

A. +98   B. +78   C. -78   D. -98 .

8. The enthalpies of combustion of C(s), $H_2(g)$ and $C_4H_9OH(l)$, in kJ mol^{-1}, are :

C(s)	+	$O_2(g)$	→	$CO_2(g)$	ΔH = **a**
$H_2(g)$	+	$^1/_2 O_2(g)$	→	$H_2O(l)$	ΔH = **b**
$C_4H_9OH(l)$ +	$6O_2(g)$	→	$4CO_2(g)$ +	5 $H_2O(l)$	ΔH = **c**

What is the enthalpy of formation, in kJ mol^{-1}, of butanol?

A. 4**a** + 5**b** - **c**
B. 2**a** + 10**b** - **c**
C. **c** - 4**a** - 5**b**
D. 2**a** + 5**b** + **c**

9. The table shows the enthalpies of combustion (ΔH_c) and formation (ΔH_f) for ethene and ethane.

Compound	ΔH_c	ΔH_f
Ethene	ΔH_1	ΔH_3
Ethane	ΔH_2	ΔH_4

The enthalpy change for the reaction

$C_2H_4(g)$ + $H_2(g)$ → $C_2H_6(g)$ is

A. ΔH_1 - ΔH_2
B. ΔH_2 - ΔH_1
C. ΔH_3 - ΔH_4
D. ΔH_4 - ΔH_3.

10. Consider the reaction pathway shown.

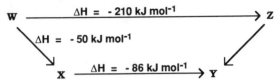

According to Hess's Law, the ΔH value, in kJ mol^{-1}, for reaction **Z** to **Y** is

A. 74   **B.** -74   **C.** +346   **D.** -346.

11. What is the enthalpy of formation, in kJ, of one mole of hydrogen chloride?
(Use the bond enthalpies given in the data booklet.)

A. -91.5   **B.** +91.5   **C.** 193   **D.** +183

12. What is the mean bond enthalpy, in kJ mol^{-1}, of the C-H bond in methane, CH_4?

(Use the enthalpy of formation of methane, and other information in the data booklet.)

A. 269   **B.** 306.5   **C.** 378   **D.** 415.5

13. $CH_2 - CH_2$ + HBr → $CH_3CH_2CH_2Br$ ΔH = -3 kJ mol^{-1}
     \ /
     CH_2

What is the mean bond enthalpy, in kJ mol^{-1}, of the C-C bond in cyclopropane?
(Use the bond enthalpies given in the data booklet.)

A. 234   **B.** 325   **C.** 331   **D.** 369

14. Consider the bond enthalpies.

Bond	Enthalpy / kJ mol^{-1}
Br - Br	194
H - Br	366
C - H	414
C - Br	280

    H H   H H
    | | | |
H-C-C-H   + Br - Br   →   H-C-C-Br   + H - Br
    | | | |
    H H   H H

What is the enthalpy change, in kJ mol^{-1}, for the reaction?

A. +38   **B.** -38   **C.** -1254   **D.** +1254

Test 6.6

Ionisation energy and electron gain enthalpy

Questions 1 to 5 refer to what happens when an atom **X** of an element in Group 1 reacts to become an ion **X**$^+$.

Decide whether each of the statements is

A. TRUE   **B.** FALSE.

1. The diameter increases.

2. The nucleus acquires a negative charge.

3. The number of energy levels (electron shells) decreases by one.

4. The atomic number decreases by one.

5. An electron is emitted from the nucleus.

Questions 6 to 10 refer to what happens when an atom **Y** of an element in Group 7 reacts to become an ion **Y**$^-$.

Decide whether each of the statments is

A. TRUE   **B.** FALSE.

6. The diameter increases.

7. The charge of the nucleus does not change.

8. The atomic number increases by one.

9. The number of energy levels (electron shells) increases by one.

10. The number of neutrons does not change.

11. Which equation represents the first ionisation energy of calcium?

A. $1/_2Ca_{(g)}$ $\rightarrow$ $1/_2Ca^{2+}_{(g)}$ $+$ e
B. $Ca_{(s)}$ $\rightarrow$ $Ca^{2+}_{(aq)}$ $+$ $2e$
C. $Ca_{(g)}$ $\rightarrow$ $Ca^+_{(g)}$ $+$ e
D. $Ca_{(s)}$ $\rightarrow$ $Ca^+_{(aq)}$ $+$ e

12. Which equation represents the first ionisation energy of fluorine?

A. $F(g)$ + e → $F^-(g)$

B. $F(g)$ → $F^+(g)$ + e

C. $1/2F_2(g)$ → $F^-(g)$ + e

D. $F^+(g)$ + e → $F(g)$

13. Which equation represents the electron gain enthalpy of chlorine?

A. $Cl^+(g)$ + e → $1/2Cl_2(g)$

B. $1/2Cl_2(g)$ + e → $Cl^-(g)$

C. $Cl^+(g)$ + e → $Cl(g)^*$

D. $Cl(g)$ + e → $Cl^-(g)$

Questions 14 and 15 refer to the ionisation energies of four elements

	1st Ionisation energy/kJ mol^{-1}	2nd Ionisation energy/kJ mol^{-1}	3rd Ionisation energy/kJ mol^{-1}
A.	1690	3380	6060
B.	500	4560	6920
C.	600	1160	4930
D.	580	1830	2760

14. Which element is most likely to form an ion of the type X^+?

15. Which element is most likely to form an ion of the type X^{2+}?

Test 7.1   pH scale

In questions 1 to 12 decide whether each of the statements is

A. TRUE   **B.** FALSE.

1. pH 2 contains more H^+(aq) than OH^-(aq).
2. pH 6 contains more H^+(aq) than pH 4.
3. pH 5 contains H^+(aq) but **no** OH^-(aq).
4. pH 10 contains more OH^-(aq) than H^+(aq).
5. pH 11 contains **both** H^+(aq) and OH^-(aq).
6. pH 9 contains more OH^-(aq) than pH 11.
7. pH 7 contains more H^+(aq) than OH^-(aq).
8. pH 6 contains an equal concentration of H^+(aq) and OH^-(aq).
9. pH 4 is more acidic than pH 6.
10. pH 8 is more alkaline than pH 10.
11. An acid can have a pH value of 3.8.
12. An alkali can have a pH value of 10.4.

In questions 13 to 20 decide the pH value of each of the solutions.

A. -1 **B.** 0 **C.** 1 **D.** 4 **E.** 9 **F.** 12 **G.** 14 **H.** 15

13. 0.1 mol l^{-1} hydrochloric acid
14. 0.0001 mol l^{-1} nitric acid
15. 0.01 mol l^{-1} sodium hydroxide solution
16. 0.00001 mol l^{-1} potassium hydroxide solution
17. 1 mol l^{-1} hydrochloric acid
18. 1 mol l^{-1} sodium hydroxide solution
19. 10 mol l^{-1} potassium hydroxide solution
20. 10 mol l^{-1} nitric acid

In questions 21 to 23 decide the concentration of hydrogen ions, in mol l^{-1}, in solutions with each of the pH values.

A. 10^{-2} **B.** 10^{-5} **C.** 10^{-7} **D.** 10^{-9} **E.** 10^{-12}

21. 5   22. 7   23. 12

In questions 24 to 26 decide the concentration of hydroxide ions, in mol l^{-1}, in solutions with each of the pH values.

A. 10^{-1} **B.** 10^{-4} **C.** 10^{-7} **D.** 10^{-10} **E.** 10^{-13}

24. 4   25. 7   26. 13

Test 7.2   pH of solutions

The questions in this test refer to the pH of solutions.

A. less than 7   **B.** equal to 7   **C.** more than 7

What is the pH of an aqueous solution of each of the substances?

1. hydrogen chloride
2. ammonia
3. sulphur dioxide
4. carbon dioxide
5. methylamine
6. sodium chloride
7. ammonium nitrate
8. lithium sulphate
9. potassium ethanoate
10. ammonium chloride
11. sodium sulphite
12. potassium carbonate
13. magnesium nitrate
14. sodium tartrate
15. barium chloride

Test 7.3   Strong and weak acids and bases

Questions 1 to 6 refer to equal volumes of 0.1 mol l^{-1} hydrochloric acid and 0.1 mol l^{-1} ethanoic acid.

Decide whether each of the statements is

A. TRUE   **B.** FALSE .

1. They give the same colour with Universal indicator
2. They have a pH less than 7.
3. They conduct electricity equally well.
4. They have equal concentrations of hydrogen ions.
5. They react at the same rate with magnesium.
6. They neutralise the same number of moles of sodium hydroxide.

Questions 7 and 8 refer to 0.1 mol l^{-1} acidic solutions.

A. hydrochloric acid   **B.** ethanoic acid
C. sulphuric acid   **D.** nitric acid

7. Which solution has the lowest conductivity?

8. Which solution has the highest pH?

9. The conductivity of 1 mol l^{-1} nitric acid is higher than the conductivity of 1 mol l^{-1} ethanoic acid.

This is because

A. nitric acid is a concentrated acid
B. ethanoic acid contains more water molecules
C. ethanoic acid is a dilute acid
D. nitric acid contains more H^{+}(aq) ions.

10. Which statement is **not** true of sulphuric, nitric, hydrochloric and ethanoic acid?

A. They react with magnesium.
B. They are completely dissociated in aqueous solution.
C. They react with alkalis.
D. In aqueous solution they have a pH less than 7.

11. Which statement is correct?

    0.1 mol l^{-1} ethanoic acid is

    A. a weak solution of a strong acid
    B. a strong solution of a weak acid
    C. a dilute solution of a weak acid
    D. a weak solution of a dilute acid.

12. Which statement is correct?

    0.1 mol l^{-1} hydrochloric acid is

    A. a weak solution of a strong acid
    B. a dilute solution of a strong acid
    C. a weak solution of a weak acid
    D. a dilute solution of a weak acid.

Questions 13 to 17 refer to equal volumes of 0.1 mol l^{-1} sodium hydroxide solution and 0.1 mol l^{-1} ammonia solution.

Decide whether each of the statements is

A. TRUE   **B.** FALSE.

13. They give the same colour with Universal indicator.

14. They conduct electricity equally well.

15. They have a pH greater than 7.

16. They contain equal numbers of hydroxide ions.

17. They neutralise the same number of moles of hydrochloric acid.

Questions 18 and 19 refer to 0.1 mol l^{-1} alkaline solutions .

A. sodium hydroxide   **B.** ammonium hydroxide
C. potassium hydroxide   **D.** lithium hydroxide

18. Which solution has the lowest pH?

19. Which solution has the lowest conductivity?

Test 7.4

Equilibrium (i)

Questions 1 to 5 refer to reversible reactions at equilibrium.

Decide whether each of the statements is

 A. TRUE   **B.** FALSE.

1. The concentrations of reactants are always equal to the concentrations of products.

2. The concentrations of reactants and products are constant.

3. Molecules of reactants have ceased to change into molecules of products.

4. The rates of forward and reverse reactions are equal.

5. The activation energies of the forward and reverse reactions are equal.

Questions 6 to 10 refer to the role of catalysts in reversible reactions.

Decide whether each of the statements is

 A. TRUE   **B.** FALSE.

6. Catalysts decrease the time required for the equilibrium to be established.

7. Catalysts alter the position of equilibrium.

8. Catalysts lower the activation energy of the forward reactions.

9. Catalysts increase the rate of the reverse reactions.

10. Catalysts increase the activation energy of the reverse reactions.

Questions 11 to 14 refer to a reversible reaction at equilibrium.

Decide whether each of the following

 A. influences the position of equilibrium
 B. does **NOT** influence the position of equilibrium.

11. particle size

12. reactant concentration

13. catalytic action

14. temperature change

Test 7.5 Equilibrium (ii)

Questions 1 to 3 refer to the equilibrium :

$$N_2(g) \quad + \quad 3H_2(g) \rightleftharpoons 2NH_3(g)$$

Changing the concentration of reactants and products can

A. move the equilibrium to the right
B. move the equilibrium to the left.

Decide how the equilibrium mixture would be affected by each of the changes.

1. increasing the concentration of nitrogen gas
2. decreasing the concentration of hydrogen gas
3. decreasing the concentration of ammonia gas

Questions 4 to 9 refer to the equilibrium:

$$Cl_2(aq) \quad + \quad H_2O(g) \rightleftharpoons 2H^+(aq) \quad + \quad ClO^-(aq) \quad + \quad Cl^-(aq)$$

The addition of substances can

A. move the equilibrium to the product side
B. move the equilibrium to the reactant side
C. leave the equilibrium mixture unchanged.

Decide the effect of adding each of the substances.

4. sodium chloride crystals
5. nitric acid
6. potassium sulphate crystals
7. silver nitrate solution
8. sodium hydroxide solution
9. potassium nitrate solution

Questions 10 to 15 refer to the effect of an increase in pressure on chemical reactions at equilibrium.

An increase in pressure can

A. increase the concentration of reactants
B. increase the concentration of products
C. have no effect on the concentration of reactants and products.

Decide the effect of an increase in pressure in each of the reactions.

10. $N_2O_{4(g)}$ ⇌ $2NO_{2(g)}$

11. $H_{2(g)}$ + $I_{2(g)}$ ⇌ $2HI_{(g)}$

12. $2SO_{2(g)}$ + $O_{2(g)}$ ⇌ $2SO_{3(g)}$

13. $NH_{3(g)}$ + $H_2O_{(g)}$ ⇌ $NH_4^+{(aq)}$ + $OH^-{(aq)}$

14. $CO_{(g)}$ + $H_2O_{(g)}$ ⇌ $CO_{2(g)}$ + $H_{2(g)}$

15. $C_{(s)}$ + $H_2O_{(g)}$ ⇌ $H_{2(g)}$ + $CO_{(g)}$

Questions 16 to 19 refer to the effect of a change in temperature on chemical reactions at equilibrium.

A change in temperature can

A. increase the concentration of reactants
B. increase the concentration of products.

What will be the effect of the temperature change in each of the reactions.

16. temperature increase
$PCl_{5(g)}$ ⇌ $PCl_{3(g)}$ + $Cl_{2(g)}$ $\Delta H = -92 \text{ kJ mol}^{-1}$

17. temperature decrease
$2NO_{(g)}$ ⇌ $N_{2(g)}$ + $O_{2(g)}$ $\Delta H = -180 \text{ kJ mol}^{-1}$

18. temperature increase
$H_2O_{(g)}$ ⇌ $2H_{2(g)}$ + $O_{2(g)}$ $\Delta H = +484 \text{ kJ mol}^{-1}$

19. temperature decrease
$KBr_{(s)}$ + (aq) ⇌ $K^+{(aq)}$ + $Br^-{(aq)}$ $\Delta H = +20 \text{ kJ mol}^{-1}$

Questions 20 to 22 refer to the equilibrium:

$$C_2H_{4(g)} \quad + \quad H_{2(g)} \quad \rightleftharpoons \quad C_2H_{6(g)}$$

ΔH for the forward reaction = -138 kJ mol^{-1}

Decide whether each of the changes will

A. increase the equilibrium concentration of $C_2H_{6(g)}$

B. decrease the equilibrium concentration of $C_2H_{6(g)}$.

20. increase in pressure

21. addition of $H_{2(g)}$

22. increase in temperature

Test 7.6

Equilibrium (iii)

1. 0.1 mol of methanol, 0.1 mol of ethanoic acid and a few drops of concentrated sulphuric acid were warmed together. After a considerable time the reaction mixture was found still to contain some of each of the reactants as well as some ester.

   What is the best explanation of the incomplete reaction?

   A. An equilibrium mixture was formed.
   B. The temperature was too low.
   C. Insufficient methanol was used.
   D. Insufficient catalyst was used.

2. Hydrogen and iodine at 500 °C react according to the equation:

   $$H_{2(g)} \quad + \quad I_{2(g)} \quad \rightleftharpoons \quad 2HI_{(g)}$$

   Vessel **X** initially contains 1 mol H_2 + 1 mol I_2; vessel **Y** initially contains 2 mol HI.
   X and **Y** are left at 500 °C until no further change occurs.

   Which statement is then true?

   A. **X** will contain more hydrogen than **Y**.
   B. **X** will contain less iodine than **Y**.
   C. **X** and **Y** will contain the same amount of hydrogen iodide.
   D. **Y** will contain 1 mol of iodine.

   Questions 3 and 4 refer to the addition of compounds to the equilibrium:

   $$Ag^+_{(aq)} \quad + \quad Fe^{2+}_{(aq)} \quad \rightleftharpoons \quad Ag_{(s)} \quad + \quad Fe^{3+}_{(aq)}$$

A. hydrochloric acid	**B.** iron(III) hydroxide
C. iron(II) sulphate	**D.** sulphuric acid

3. Which compound when added to the equilibrium mixture, would lead to an increase in the mass of silver deposited?

4. Which compound when added to the equilibrium mixture, would lead more silver dissolving?

5. $C_2H_4(g)$ + $H_2(g)$ $\rightleftharpoons$ $C_2H_6(g)$ ΔH is -ve

Which procedure would not affect the position of equilibrium?

    A.   decreasing the pressure
    B.   decreasing the temperature
    C.   adding a catalyst
    D.   adding more hydrogen

6. $2SO_2(g)$ + $O_2(g)$ $\rightleftharpoons$ $2SO_3(g)$

In the presence of a catalyst the equilibrium yield would be

    A.   increased and attained more rapidly
    B.   increased and attained in the same time
    C.   unchanged but attained more rapidly
    D.   decreased but attained more rapidly.

Questions 7 and 8 refer to reactions at equilibrium.

    A. $2CO(g)$ + $O_2(g)$ $\rightleftharpoons$ $CO_2(g)$
    B. $H_2(g)$ + $Cl_2(g)$ $\rightleftharpoons$ $2HCl(g)$
    C. $PCl_5(g)$ $\rightleftharpoons$ $PCl_3(g)$ + $Cl_2(g)$
    D. $2NO_2(g)$ $\rightleftharpoons$ $N_2O_4(g)$

7. For which reaction will the proportion of product present at equilibrium be increased as the pressure is lowered?

8. For which reaction will the equilibrium be unaffected by a change in pressure?

Questions 9 and 10 refer to the most favourable conditions for reactions.

    A.   high temperature, high pressure
    B.   high temperature, low pressure
    C.   low temperature, high pressure
    D.   low temperature, low pressure

9. $2NO(g)$ + $O_2(g)$ $\rightleftharpoons$ $2NO_2(g)$ $\Delta H = -560$ kJ mol^{-1}

Which conditions favour the formation of NO_2?

10. $CH_4(g)$ + $H_2O(g)$ $\rightleftharpoons$ $CO(g)$ + $3H_2(g)$ $\Delta H = 206$ kJ mol^{-1}

Which conditions favour the formation of hydrogen?

11. The reaction represented by the equation is exothermic.

$$3H_2(g) \quad + \quad N_2(g) \quad \rightleftharpoons \quad 2NH_3(g)$$

In the presence of the appropriate catalyst which set of conditions would give the best yield of ammonia at equilibrium?

A. 800 atmospheres and 2000 ^oC

B. 1 atmosphere and 2000 ^oC

C. 1 atmosphere and 500 ^oC

D. 800 atmospheres and 500 ^oC

12. Which entry in the table shows the effect of a catalyst on the reaction rates and position of equilibrium in a reversible reaction?

	Rate of forward reaction	Rate of reverse reaction	Position of equilibrium
A.	increased	increased	unchanged
B.	increased	unchanged	changed
C.	increased	decreased	changed
D.	unchanged	unchanged	unchanged

13. Excess sodium chloride was shaken with water, giving a saturated solution with some solid sodium chloride on the bottom of the container.

$$NaCl(s) \quad \rightleftharpoons \quad Na^+(aq) \quad + \quad Cl^-(aq)$$

What will happen if $HCl(g)$ is passed through the solution?

A. Chlorine gas will form.

B. The pH will rise.

C. Some sodium chloride will crystallise out.

D. Some solid sodium chloride will dissolve.

14. The decomposition of magnesium carbonate by heat can be prevented from going to completion by

A. absorbing the carbon dioxide produced in lime water

B. removing magnesium oxide as it is formed

C. carrying out the reaction in a small, closed vessel

D. reducing the pressure in the reaction vessel.

Test 8.1

1. Isotopes of the same element must have

   A. the same number of protons and neutrons, but different numbers of electrons
   B. the same number of protons and electrons, but different numbers of neutrons
   C. the same number of neutrons, but different numbers of protons and electrons
   D. the same number of protons, but different numbers of electrons and neutrons.

2. Some atoms of an element are heavier than other atoms of the same element.
   This is because they have different numbers of

   A. neutrons   B. protons   C. nuclei   D. electrons.

3. Which of the following statements is **not** true about isotopes?

   A. Their electron arrangements are the same.
   B. The masses of their nuclei are different.
   C. Their numbers of protons are different.
   D. Their nuclear charges are the same.

4. Which statement **cannot** be true of two atoms with the same mass number?

   A. They are isotopes of the same element.
   B. They have different numbers of protons.
   C. They have different numbers of neutrons.
   D. They are atoms of two different elements.

5. The two isotopes of carbon, $^{12}_{6}C$ and $^{14}_{6}C$, differ from each other in

   A. mass number   B. atomic number
   C. chemical properties   D. electron arrangement.

6. An isotope of oxygen of mass number 18 differs from the most abundant form of oxygen in

   A. the number of atoms per molecule
   B. the number of electrons in the outer energy level (shell)
   C. the number of protons in each nucleus
   D. the proportion of protons to neutrons in the nucleus.

In question 7 to 12 decide whether each of the pairs

A.   are isotopes of the same element

B.   are **NOT** isotopes of the same element.

7. an atom with 6 protons and 8 neutrons
and
an atom with 8 protons and 8 neutrons

8. an atom with 10 protons and 10 neutrons
and
an atom with 10 protons and 12 neutrons

9. an atom with atomic number 17 and mass number 35
and
an atom with atomic number 17 and mass number 37

10. an atom with atomic number 1 and mass number 2
and
an atom with atomic number 2 and mass number 4

11. $^{16}_{8}\mathbf{W}$ and $^{18}_{8}\mathbf{X}$

12. $^{40}_{19}\mathbf{Y}$ and $^{40}_{20}\mathbf{Z}$

13. Which pair or pairs of atoms are isotopes of the same element?

$^{86}_{38}\mathbf{W}$ $^{86}_{36}\mathbf{X}$ $^{87}_{38}\mathbf{Y}$ $^{87}_{37}\mathbf{Z}$

A.   **W,X** only   **B.**   **W,Y** only
C.   **W,X** and **Y,Z**   **D.**   no pair

14. Information about the atomic structure of atoms is given in the table.

Atom	Number of neutrons in the nucleus	Nuclear charge
1	50	36
2	50	37
3	49	38
4	52	38

Which pair of atoms are isotopes?

A.   1 and 2   **B.**   2 and 3
C.   2 and 4   **D.**   3 and 4

15. An isotope of an element can be represented $^{50}_{24}X$.

Which of the following represents another isotope of the element?

A. $^{50}_{23}X$ **B.** $^{52}_{24}X$ **C.** $^{50}_{25}X$ **D.** $^{52}_{25}X$

16. The relative atomic mass of an element is rarely a whole number.

This is because

A. different atoms of an element can have different numbers of protons
B. it is difficult to isolate pure elements
C. chemical methods of determining the relative atomic masses of elements are inaccurate
D. different atoms of an element can have different numbers of neutrons.

17. An element consists of two isotopes with mass numbers 40 and 42.

The relative atomic mass must be

A. 41 exactly
B. more than 41
C. less than 41
D. between 40 and 42, but impossible to specify.

18. The relative atomic mass of lithium is 6.94 amu.

This is because

A. all lithium atoms have a mass of 6.94 amu
B. most lithium atoms have a mass of 7 amu but a few have a mass of 6 amu
C. most lithium atoms have a mass of 6 amu but a few have a mass of 7 amu
D. most lithium atoms have a mass of 7 amu but a few have lost an electron.

19. Copper has two isotopes, each with a percentage abundance as shown.

    63Cu 75%   65Cu 25%

What is the approximate relative atomic mass of copper?

A. 63   **B.** 63.5   **C.** 64   **D.** 65

20. Naturally occurring gallium (atomic number 31, relative atomic mass 69.7) consists of a mixture of two isotopes of mass numbers 69 and 71.

Identify the true statement.

A. Atoms of gallium 69 are more abundant than those of gallium 71.
B. Atoms of the two isotopes of gallium have different numbers of protons.
C. Atoms of the two isotopes of gallium have the same number of neutrons.
D. All gallium atoms have an atomic mass of 69.7 amu.

21. The relative abundances of the two isotopes of boron are shown in the table.

Isotope	Relative abundance/%
^{10}B	18.7
^{11}B	81.3

What is the relative atomic mass of boron?

A. 10.6   B. 10.7   C. 10.8   D. 10.9

22. Naturally occurring nitrogen consists of two isotopes ^{14}N and ^{15}N.

How many types of stable nitrogen moleules will occur in the air?

A. 1   B. 2   C. 3   D. 4

23. 1 $(^{1}H_2{}^{16}O)$ 2 $(^{1}H_2{}^{17}O)$ 3 $(^{1}H_2{}^{18}O)$

  4 $(^{2}H_2{}^{16}O)$ 5 $(^{2}H_2{}^{17}O)$ 6 $(^{2}H_2{}^{18}O)$

Which pair of molecules have the same molecular mass?

A. 1 and 4   B. 2 and 5   C. 3 and 6   D. 3 and 4

Questions 24 and 25 refer to chlorine which has two isotopes,
$^{35}_{17}Cl$ and $^{37}_{17}Cl$.

24. If chlorine molecules are analysed, how many different molecular masses will be detected?

A. 1   B. 2   C. 3   D. 4

25. If chlorine molecules are analysed, which molecular mass will not be found?

A. 70   B. 71   C. 72   D. 74

26. Hydrogen has two main isotopes.

Isotope	Symbol	Mass number	Atomic number
Hydrogen	H	1	1
Deuterium	D	2	1

Which pair of ions have the same molecular mass?

A. H^+ and D^+

B. H_2^+ and D_2^+

C. H_2^+ and D^+

D. H_2^+ and HD^+

27. The chloride of a trivalent element is analysed.
The element has one isotope and chlorine has two, $^{35}_{17}Cl$ and $^{37}_{17}Cl$.

Molecules are found with mass numbers 180, 182, 184 and 186.

What is the mass number of the element?

A. 75   B. 77   C. 79   D. 81

Test 8.2   Types of radiation

The questions in this test refer to types of radiation.

A.   alpha radiation   B.   beta radiation   C.   gamma radiation

1. What name is given to the electrons which are emitted from the nucleus of certain radioactive atoms?

2. What name is given to the particles consisting of 2 protons and 2 neutrons?

3. What name is given to the electromagnetic radiations of a very short wavelength?

4. Which is the most penetrating radiation?

5. Which is the least penetrating radiation?

6. Which radation is attracted by a positive electric field?

7. Which radiation is attracted by a negative electric field?

8. Which radiation passes through an electric field without deflection?

9. What radiation is represented by $_{-1}^{0}e$?

10. What radiation is represented by $_{2}^{4}He^{2+}$?

11. Which radiation has no mass associated with it?

Test 8.3   Changes in the nucleus

Questions 1 to 5 refer to changes in the nucleus.

	Atomic number	Mass number
A.	increased	no change
B.	decreased	decreased
C.	no change	increased
D.	no change	no change
E.	increased	increased

Describe the change which is associated with each nuclear reaction.

1. beta emission

2. neutron capture

3. alpha emission

4. gamma emission

5. proton capture

6. When an atom of $^{239}_{92}U$ emits a beta particle, the product formed also decays, emitting another beta particle.

The atom formed after the second emission is

  A. $^{231}_{88}Ra$ **B.** $^{237}_{90}Th$ **C.** $^{237}_{92}U$ **D.** $^{239}_{94}Pu.$

7. Radioactive $^{14}_{6}C$ decays by beta particle emission.

Which statement is true of the new nucleus formed?

  A. It has mass number 13.
  B. It has 6 protons.
  C. It has 7 neutrons.
  D. It is a carbon nucleus.

8. $^{27}_{13}Al$ can absorb an alpha particle with the emission of a neutron.

What is the product of this reaction?

  A. $^{30}_{14}Si$ **B.** $^{28}_{15}P$ **C.** $^{30}_{15}P$ **D.** $^{31}_{16}S$

9. What is produced when a $^{35}_{17}Cl$ atom captures a neutron and then emits gamma radiation?

   A. $^{36}_{18}Ar$ **B.** $^{36}_{17}Cl$ **C.** $^{35}_{18}Ar$ **D.** $^{31}_{15}P$

10. During neutron bombardment of $^{24}_{12}Mg$, some atoms capture a neutron at the same time emitting a proton.

    What is formed?

    A. $^{23}_{12}Mg$ **B.** $^{23}_{11}Na$ **C.** $^{24}_{11}Na$ **D.** $^{26}_{13}Al$

11. What is formed when an atom of $^{239}_{92}U$ emits a beta particle?

    A. $^{240}_{91}Pa$ **B.** $^{239}_{91}Pa$ **C.** $^{239}_{93}Np$ **D.** $^{238}_{92}U$

12. Which series of transformations would produce an atom of the same element as at the start?

    A. alpha,beta,beta
    B. beta,alpha,alpha
    C. alpha,beta,gamma
    D. alpha,beta,neutron capture

13. When $^{27}_{13}Al$ is bombarded by alpha particles, an isotope of phosphorus, $^{30}_{15}P$, is formed and a particle is emitted.

    What is this particle?

    A. a beta particle   **B.** an alpha particle
    C. a proton   **D.** a neutron

    Questions 14 and 15 refer to types of particle involved in nuclear reactions.

    A. an alpha particle   **B.** a beta particle
    C. a proton   **D.** a neutron

    What is the unknown particle in each of the reactions?

14. $^{207}_{82}Pb$ +   ?   → $^{208}_{83}Bi$

15. $^{137}_{56}Ba$ + ^{1}n → $^{138}_{57}La$ +   ?

Questions 16 to 19 refer to processes occurring in nuclear tranformations.

A. alpha emission   **B.** proton capture
C. beta emission   **D.** neutron capture

Which process takes place in each of the transformations?

16. $_{1}^{3}\text{H}$ $\rightarrow$ $_{2}^{3}\text{He}$

17. $_{11}^{23}\text{Na}$ $\rightarrow$ $_{11}^{24}\text{Na}$

18. $_{84}^{210}\text{Po}$ $\rightarrow$ $_{82}^{206}\text{Pb}$

19. $_{82}^{207}\text{Pb}$ $\rightarrow$ $_{83}^{208}\text{Bi}$

20. What sequence of particles is emitted?

$_{91}^{231}\text{Pa}$ $\rightarrow$ $_{89}^{227}\text{Ac}$ $\rightarrow$ $_{90}^{227}\text{Th}$

A. an alpha particle and then a neutron
B. an alpha particle and then a beta particle
C. a beta particle and then an alpha particle
D. a beta particle and then a proton

21. What particle will be formed when an atom of $_{83}^{211}\text{Bi}$ loses an alpha particle and the decay product then loses a beta particle?

A. $_{79}^{210}\text{Au}$ **B.** $_{80}^{209}\text{Hg}$ **C.** $_{81}^{207}\text{Tl}$ **D.** $_{82}^{207}\text{Pb}$

Test 8.4   Half-life

1. The half-life of tritium, ^3_1H is 12.4 years. In a bottle of old wine, the ^3_1H level is found to be $1/16$ th of that in new wine.

   The wine was approximately

   A. 40 years old   B. 60 years old
   C. 50 years old   D. 100 years old.

2. $^{24}_{11}Na$ is a beta emitter with a half-life of 15 hours.

   What percentage of the original isotope would remain after 45 hours?

   A. 12.5   B. 25   C. 75   D. 87.5

3. $^{210}_{84}Po$ is an alpha emitter with a half-life of 140 days. A sample of the isotope was analysed and the chart shown was obtained.

   What is the age of the isotope?

   A. 140 days
   B. 280 days
   C. 420 days
   D. 840 days

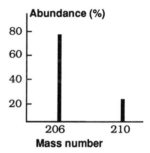

4. When some zinc pellets containing radioactive zinc are placed in a solution of zinc chloride, radioactivity soon appears in the solution.

   Compared to the pellets, the half-life of the radioactive solution will be

   A. shorter   B. the same   C. longer
   D. dependent upon how long the zinc is in contact with the solution.

5. After 15 days a sample contained 7.5×10^{23} atoms of radioactive bismuth, half-life 5 days.

   How many atoms were in the sample originally?

   A. 2.25×10^{23} B. 2.5×10^{23}
   C. 3.75×10^{23} D. 6.0×10^{24}

6. After 48 years the level of radioactivity in a sample of an isotope was found to be $1/8$ th of the level originally.

What is the half-life of the isotope?

   A. 6 years   **B.** 12 years   **C.** 16 years   **D.** 24 years

7. $^{215}_{81}$Tl is a beta emitter with a half-life of 4.2 minutes.

What percentage of the original isotope would remain after 8.4 minutes?

   A. 12.5   **B.** 25   **C.** 50   **D.** 75

8. When some lead pellets containing radioactive lead are placed in a solution of lead nitrate, radioactivity soon appears in the solution.

Compared to the pellets the solution will show

   A. different intensity of radiation and different half-life
   B. the same intensity of radiation but different half-life
   C. different intensity of radiation but the same half-life
   D. the same intensity of radiation and the same half-life.

9. The chart shown was obtained from a 12 day old sample of an alpha emitting radioactive isotope.

What is the half-life of the isotope?

   A. 2 days   **B.** 3 days
   C. 4 days   **D.** 6 days

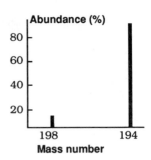

10. $^{224}_{88}$Ra is an alpha emitter.

In which of the following will the half-life be shortest?

   A. 1 g of radium   **B.** 10 g of radium
   C. 1 g of radium chloride   **D.** none of these

Questions 11 and 12 refer to different radioisotopes.

A. half-life 2.1 years , beta emitter
B. half-life 1620 years, alpha emitter
C. half-life 3.92 seconds, alpha emitter
D. half-life 1.6 minutes, gamma emitter

11. Which radioisotope could be involved in the dating of archaeological objects?

12. Which radioisotope could be used to detect cracks under the surface of a metal pipe?

13. ^{14}C has a half-life of 5600 years.   An analysis of charcoal from a wood fire shows that its ^{14}C content is 25% that of living wood.

How many years have passed since the wood for the fire was cut?

A. 1400   **B.** 4200   **C.** 11 200   **D.** 16 800

14. Radioactive uranium is present in rocks in the form of compounds like uranium(IV) oxide.   When the rock is processed, a large amount of the uranium can be recovered as pure metal.

Compared to the original rock, the half-life of the pure metal will be

A. shorter
B. the same
C. longer
D. dependent upon the amount that is recovered.

15. $^{210}_{84}Po$ is an alpha emitter with a half-life of 140 days.

What percentage of the original isotope would remain after 420 days?

A. 12.5   **B.** 25   **C.** 75   **D.** 87.5

16. Which, if any, of the following processes would alter the half-life of a sample of radioactive calcium?

A. cooling it to -50 ºC   **B.** dissolving it in dilute hydrochloric acid

C. burning it in air   **D.** none of these

17. The half-life of the isotope ^{14}C is 5.6×10^3 years.

What fraction of the original ^{14}C atoms will remain after 2.24×10^4 years?

A. 0.5   **B.** 0.25   **C.** 0.125   **D.** 0.0625

Test 1.1	Test 1.2	Test 1.3		Test 2.1	
1. A	1. C	1. C		1. AC	19. D
2. B	2. B	2. D		2. AC	20. C
3. B	3. D	3. A		3. BD	21. C
4. A	4. C	4. C		4. AC	22. A
5. B	5. B	5. B		5. AC	23. B
6. B	6. B	6. C		6. BD	24. A
7. A	7. C	7. A		7. BD	25. C
8. B	8. C	8. D		8. BD	26. C
9. A	9. A	9. C		9. AC	27. C
10. A	10. B	10. D		10. AC	28. A
11. B	11. A	11. B		11. BD	29. D
12. A	12. C	12. D		12. AC	30. D
13. B	13. A	13. D		13. C	31. D
14. A	14. C	14. C		14. G	32. C
15. B	15. A	15. C		15. A	33. A
16. A	16. B	16. B		16. D	34. C
17. A	17. D	17. D		17. H	35. C
18. B	18. A	18. D		18. J	36. B
19. B	19. C	19. D			
20. A	20. B	20. B			
21. B	21. C	21. A			
22. A	22. B	22. C			
23. B	23. C	23. D			
24. B	24. C	24. C			
	25. C	25. D			
	26. A				

Test 2.2	Test 2.3	Test 2.4	Test 2.5	Test 2.6	
1. A	1. A	1. E	1. B	1. A	19. B
2. B	2. B	2. CF	2. A	2. B	20. A
3. B	3. B	3. G	3. A	3. A	21. A
4. A	4. B	4. C	4. A	4. B	22. B
5. B	5. A	5. EF	5. B	5. B	23. A
6. A	6. B	6. AD	6. A	6. A	24. A
7. A	7. A	7. E	7. A	7. B	25. B
8. B	8. B	8. BF	8. C	8. A	26. B
9. B	9. A	9. B	9. D	9. B	27. B
10. A	10. B	10. A	10. A	10. A	28. C
11. B	11. A	11. B	11. B	11. B	29. B
12. A	12. A	12. A	12. B	12. A	30. B
13. FH	13. B		13. A	13. A	31. A
14. DFH	14. A		14. A	14. A	32. D
15. B	15. B		15. B	15. B	33. D
16. D	16. B			16. A	34. B
17. B	17. A			17. B	35. C
18. C	18. C			18. A	36. D
19. A					
20. C					
21. D					

Test 2.7		Test 2.8	Test 2.9	Test 2.10	Test 2.11
1. B	16. B	1. CLU	1. CFG	1. A	1. B
2. B	17. A	2. BH	LN	2. B	2. B
3. A	18. B	3. FIOT	2. AEH	3. A	3. A
4. A	19. A	4. ADJ	IKMO	4. C	4. A
5. A	20. B	PR	3. BDJP	5. A	5. C
6. B	21. C			6. C	6. C
7. B	22. D			7. C	7. B
8. A	23. A			8. B	8. B
9. A	24. A			9. A	9. A
10. A	25. B			10. B	10. B
11. B	26. B			11. A	11. A
12. B	27. B			12. B	12. B
13. A	28. B			13. C	13. C
14. B	29. A			14. B	14. B
15. A				15. A	15. D
				16. B	16. A
				17. A	17. B
				18. B	18. D
				19. A	19. D
				20. B	
				21. A	
				22. B	
				23. A	
				24. B	

Test 2.12	Test 2.13	Test 2.14	Test 2.15	Test 2.16	Test 2.17
1. A	1. A	1. A	1. A	1. B	1. B
2. B	2. E	2. B	2. B	2. B	2. A
3. B	3. D	3. A	3. A	3. A	3. B
4. B	4. AB	4. B	4. A	4. A	4. A
5. A	5. AF	5. A	5. A	5. B	5. A
6. B	6. D	6. B	6. B	6. A	6. D
7. A	7. G	7. A	7. B	7. A	7. B
8. A	8. D	8. B	8. A	8. B	8. B
9. A	9. CF	9. B	9. B	9. B	9. A
10. A	10. D	10. B	10. B	10. B	10. B
11. B	11. A	11. B	11. A	11. C	11. A
12. A	12. D	12. A	12. A	12. D	12. B
13. B	13. AF	13. B	13. B	13. A	13. C
14. A	14. G	14. A	14. C	14. B	14. D
15. A	15. D	15. A	15. B	15. B	15. B
16. A	16. CF	16. A	16. A	16. A	
17. B	17. E		17. B	17. B	
18. A	18. AB		18. A	18. B	
19. B			19. B		
20. B			20. A		
			21. A		
			22. B		
			23. C		
			24. D		

Test 3.1	Test 3.2	Test 3.3	Test 3.4	Test 3.5	Test 3.6
1. B	1. A	1. B	1. A	1. B	1. B
2. B	2. A	2. A	2. C	2. A	2. A
3. D	3. A	3. B	3. D	3. B	3. A
4. D	4. B	4. B	4. C	4. B	4. A
5. D	5. C	5. A	5. B	5. A	5. B
6. A	6. B	6. A	6. D	6. B	6. B
7. C	7. D	7. D	7. B	7. A	7. A
8. C	8. B	8. B	8. C	8. A	8. A
9. B	9. C	9. C	9. A	9. A	9. D
10. A	10. C	10. B	10. B	10. B	10. B
11. D	11. C	11. B		11. B	11. A
12. A	12. B	12. B		12. B	12. C
13. D	13. B	13. C		13. A	13. C
	14. B	14. A		14. A	14. A
	15. C	15. A		15. B	15. A
	16. A	16. D		16. A	16. B
	17. D			17. B	17. B
	18. C			18. A	18. D
	19. C			19. B	19. A
	20. D			20. B	20. D
	21. C			21. B	21. C
				22. A	
				23. A	
				24. B	
				25. A	

Test 3.7	Test 3.8	Test 3.9	Test 3.10	Test 3.11
1. A	1. C	1. B	1. B	1. A
2. B	2. B	2. A	2. A	2. B
3. C	3. A	3. D	3. A	3. B
4. C	4. B	4. A	4. B	4. A
5. A	5. A	5. C	5. A	5. A
6. B	6. B		6. A	6. B
7. B	7. B		7. A	7. B
8. A	8. A		8. B	8. A
9. C	9. C		9. A	9. A
10. C	10. B		10. B	10. A
11. A	11. B		11. A	11. B
12. B	12. B		12. B	12. B
13. A	13. A			13. A
14. B	14. B			14. A
15. B	15. A			15. A
16. B	16. B			
17. B	17. C			
18. A	18. B			
	19. A			
	20. A			

Test 4.1	Test 4.2		Test 4.3	Test 4.4
1. A	1. B	15. A	1. B	1. B
2. B	2. A	16. B	2. A	2. A
3. B	3. B	17. B	3. B	3. D
4. A	4. B	18. B	4. A	4. D
5. A	5. A	19. A	5. A	5. B
6. C	6. B	20. B	6. B	6. A
7. A	7. A	21. A	7. B	7. B
8. A	8. B	22. B	8. C	8. A
9. C	9. B	23. A	9. D	9. D
10. C	10. B	24. B	10. B	10. C
11. B	11. B	25. D		11. D
12. A	12. A	26. B		12. B
13. C	13. A	27. C		
14. A	14. B	28. A		
15. C				

Test 5.1	Test 5.2		Test 5.3		Test 5.4
1. A	1. A	25. D	1. B	15. A	1. B
2. E	2. C	26. C	2. B	16. D	2. B
3. A	3. A	27. B	3. A	17. A	3. A
4. C	4. C	28. D	4. B	18. B	4. A
5. A	5. B	29. A	5. B	19. C	5. B
6. B	6. A	30. C	6. A	20. A	6. A
7. D	7. A	31. C	7. B	21. D	7. A
8. C	8. B	32. B	8. A	22. B	8. A
9. A	9. A	33. B	9. A	23. A	
10. E	10. B	34. A	10. B	24. B	
11. C	11. B	35. B	11. D	25. A	
12. A	12. B	36. A	12. D	26. B	
13. E	13. A	37. B	13. C	27. A	
14. B	14. C	38. C	14. B	28. B	
15. C	15. B	39. E			
16. D	16. A	40. B			
17. A	17. D	41. C			
18. B	18. B	42. D			
19. A	19. D	43. A			
20. C	20. B	44. C			
	21. C	45. A			
	22. C	46. A			
	23. B	47. D			
	24. A				

Test 5.5	Test 5.6		Test 5.7
1. A	1. B	20. B	1. A
2. A	2. A	21. B	2. C
3. B	3. B	22. B	3. B
4. B	4. B	23. B	4. B
5. A	5. A	24. C	5. C
6. B	6. B	25. A	6. A
7. A	7. A	26. C	7. D
8. D	8. A	27. C	8. D
	9. B	28. B	9. A
	10. A	29. B	10. C
	11. B	30. B	11. D
	12. B	31. A	12. A
	13. A	32. A	13. D
	14. A	33. A	14. D
	15. B	34. A	15. A
	16. A	35. B	16. A
	17. A	36. A	17. D
	18. A	37. B	
	19. A	38. A	

Test 6.1	Test 6.2	Test 6.3	Test 6.4	Test 6.5	Test 6.6
1. B	1. B	1. C	1. A	1. C	1. B
2. B	2. A	2. H	2. B	2. A	2. B
3. B	3. A	3. AB	3. A	3. B	3. A
4. B	4. A	4. F	4. B	4. A	4. B
5. A	5. D	5. B	5. D	5. C	5. B
6. C	6. C	6. E	6. C	6. A	6. A
7. C		7. G	7. B	7. C	7. A
8. B		8. D	8. C	8. A	8. B
9. B		9. A	9. B	9. D	9. B
10. C		10. G	10. B	10. A	10. A
11. A		11. C	11. B	11. A	11. C
12. B		12. F	12. A	12. D	12. B
		13. B	13. A	13. B	13. D
		14. C		14. B	14. B
		15. A			15. C
		16. C			
		17. B			
		18. B			
		19. A			
		20. A			

Test 7.1	Test 7.2	Test 7.3	Test 7.4	Test 7.5	Test 7.6
1. A	1. A	1. B	1. B	1. A	1. A
2. B	2. C	2. A	2. A	2. B	2. C
3. B	3. A	3. B	3. B	3. A	3. C
4. A	4. A	4. B	4. A	4. B	4. A
5. A	5. C	5. B	5. B	5. B	5. C
6. B	6. B	6. A	6. A	6. C	6. C
7. B	7. A	7. B	7. B	7. A	7. C
8. B	8. B	8. B	8. A	8. A	8. B
9. A	9. C	9. D	9. A	9. C	9. C
10. B	10. A	10. B	10. B	10. A	10. B
11. A	11. C	11. C	11. B	11. C	11. D
12. A	12. C	12. B	12. A	12. B	12. A
13. C	13. B	13. B	13. B	13. B	13. C
14. D	14. C	14. B	14. A	14. C	14. C
15. F	15. B	15. A		15. A	
16. E		16. B		16. A	
17. B		17. A		17. B	
18. G		18. B		18. B	
19. H		19. B		19. A	
20. A'				20. A	
21. B				21. A	
22. C				22. B	
23. E					
24. D					
25. C					
26. A					

Test 8.1		Test 8.2	Test 8.3	Test 8.4
1. B	15. B	1. B	1. A	1. C
2. A	16. D	2. A	2. C	2. A
3. C	17. D	3. C	3. B	3. B
4. A	18. B	4. C	4. D	4. B
5. A	19. B	5. A	5. E	5. D
6. D	20. A	6. B	6. D	6. C
7. B	21. C	7. A	7. C	7. B
8. A	22. C	8. C	8. C	8. C
9. A	23. D	9. B	9. B	9. C
10. B	24. C	10. A	10. C	10. D
11. A	25. B	11. C	11. C	11. B
12. B	26. C		12. A	12. A
13. B	27. A		13. D	13. C
14. D			14. C	14. B
			15. B	15. A
			16. C	16. D
			17. D	17. D
			18. A	
			19. B	
			20. B	
			21. D	

Answer Grid

Test ....

	answer	√		answer	√		answe	√
1.			16.			31.		
2.			17.			32.		
3.			18.			33.		
4.			19.			34.		
5.			20.			35.		
6.			21.			36.		
7.			22.			37.		
8.			23.			38.		
9.			24.			39.		
10.			25.			40.		
11.			26.			41.		
12.			27.			42.		
13.			28.			43.		
14.			29.			44.		
15.			30.			45.		

Comments:

Mark   /